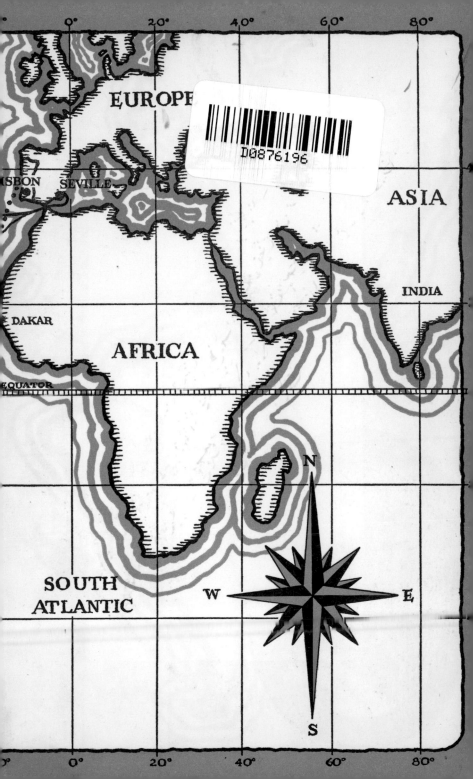

Amerigo Vespucci

AMERIGO VESPUCCI

by Nina Brown Baker

ILLUSTRATED BY PAUL VALENTINO

New York *Alfred A Knopf* 1956

Library of Congress Catalog Card Number: 56-5272

© NINA BROWN BAKER, 1956

THIS IS A BORZOI BOOK,
PUBLISHED BY ALFRED A. KNOPF, INC.

FIRST EDITION

Contents

I	*The Stars Above*	3
II	*In the Cloister*	13
III	*Amerigo the Businessman*	23
IV	*Admiral of the Ocean Sea*	35
V	*The Admiral Is in Trouble*	48
VI	*Amerigo the Explorer*	55
VII	*The Tree-walled Coast*	65
VIII	*Every Day Is Friday*	73
IX	*Downfall of the Admiral*	84
X	*Under a New Flag*	97
XI	*A New Name on the Map*	114
XII	*The Last Journey*	127
	BIBLIOGRAPHY	143
	INDEX	*follows* 144

Amerigo Vespucci

The Stars Above

HE did not really have the whole world to himself. It only seemed so, up here on this lonely hilltop, high above the village.

If he looked down, he could see the torches blazing in the little square. He could hear the gay dance music, and now and again snatches of song. But why should he look down? There were more wonderful sights to be seen in the velvet-dark Italian sky above him.

Absently he rubbed the back of his neck, which ached from the long craning upward. A little breeze rustled his star map, spread out on a flat stone. His candle flickered and went out. He was struggling to relight it with flint and tinder when he heard his name called. Footsteps were stumbling toward him in the darkness.

"Amerigo, are you there? You must come down at once. Uncle Giovanni wants you."

His younger brother came panting up the steep slope.

"Why do you have to climb the hill to see the stars?" he exclaimed disgustedly. "You can see them from the garden, can't you?"

"Not so well," the older boy answered seriously. "The trees get in the way. Up here I can see all the heavens spread out like a map. That's what I'm trying to do. To copy that map. But it's a long job. I only placed one constellation tonight, although I think I found Sagittarius, too. I wish I could be sure."

"How could you be sure? Sag—Sag—whatever you call him, that star can't tell you his name, can he?"

Amerigo laughed. "Not a star, a constellation. A group of stars. They form a picture of an archer with his bow bent. If you look where I'm pointing, you'll see him. If I have it right," he added cautiously. "Does it look like a man with a bow to you?"

"No, it does not. All I see is a sky full of stars. Some are brighter than others, that's all. Did you hear what I told you, Amerigo? Uncle wants you. He'll be cross if you don't come. And you're missing the dancing. The whole village is out in the square. Do come along!"

"I'm coming." Amerigo rolled his map around his candle. "I can't do any more without a light, and my tinder is damp. Tomorrow night I'll bring a lantern."

"Tomorrow night? Don't you ever get tired of watching the stars, Amerigo? They all look alike, and they always look the same. It's such a dull game to play."

"It isn't a game, and it isn't dull," Amerigo

answered. "If you'd go to Uncle Giorgio Antonio for lessons as I do, Bernardo, you'd find out how fascinating it is to study the stars."

"Not me," Bernardo answered cheerfully. "I'm going into the wool business. It's all very well for Uncle Giorgio. He's a monk, and I suppose you'll be one, too. But I shall be a businessman and make a fortune. Are you never coming? I told you Uncle Giovanni—"

"I know, I know." Amerigo slipped the rolled map into his belt, along with his quill pen and inkhorn. "I'm ready."

The two boys plunged down the hill.

"What does Uncle want with me?" Amerigo asked. "I thought he'd be celebrating with the others. There's no work to do tonight. The grape harvest is in, and the workers are paid off."

"That's just the trouble," Bernardo laughed. "Some of the workers aren't satisfied with their pay. You know our uncle. He has muddled his accounts again. He wants you to straighten them out and make sure each man gets what he earned."

"Me?" There was gentle teasing in Amerigo's voice. "But you're the businessman, Bernardo.

Why didn't you straighten the accounts for him?"

"Now, Brother, that's not fair. You know I'm not good at arithmetic. When I'm a prosperous wool merchant, I shall hire men to keep my books for me. I'll have more important things to do."

"Oh, certainly. I should have thought of that," Amerigo said solemnly. He was fond of his brother, although he found Bernardo's grand plans rather amusing. There was only a year between them. But Amerigo, at twelve, felt himself much more grown-up.

They reached the square, where the noise swelled into a cheerful din. Amerigo left his brother there and turned down a lane to their father's house.

It was the biggest house in the village, for the Vespuccis were Peretola's most important family. They were city people really, with their home at Florence, six miles away. The Peretola house was their country place, where they came to escape the summer heat.

Two poor relations, with their wives and children, lived there the year round, managing the vineyards that went with the estate. The country uncles, Giovanni and Niccolò, were easygoing good-for-nothings, and no great credit to the proud Vespucci family. The boys loved them dearly. Their happiest vacation days were spent at the farm.

Amerigo found Uncle Giovanni in the little room he used for an office. His round, red face, usually so jolly, looked distressed. He was crouched over his desk, which was covered with a litter of paper and scattered copper coins. Two burly grape-pickers lounged sullenly in the doorway.

"Not until you give us our due," one of them was saying as Amerigo came up. He said it wearily, as if he had said it many times before. "Pay us what is owing, and we leave you. Not before, though we stand here day and night until Christmas."

"But I did pay you!" Giovanni's voice was shrill. "Look, here is the record. So many baskets, so many coppers. There it is in black and white. How many times— Oh, Amerigo. I need you. These two mules complain that they earned

more than my figures show. See if you can make them see reason. I can't."

The men in the doorway moved respectfully aside for the young master. Amerigo smiled at them.

"There must be some mistake," he said soothingly. "Giulio and Antonio are honest men, Uncle, and fine workers. Let me see the figures."

He took the scribbled sheets and ran his eye rapidly over the long columns. As he had expected, it was Uncle Giovanni's addition that was at fault.

"A little mistake that anyone might make," he said gently. "This harvest has been a strain on you, Uncle; day after day in the hot sun. And on you, too, my good friends. But the toil is past now, and tonight we celebrate a fine yield. Give Giulio and Antonio their extra money, Uncle—their wives will be cross if they don't come to the square soon. As I came past, I saw that a man had come out from the city with a dancing bear. You won't want to miss that."

"A dancing bear?" Uncle Giovanni's worried look dissolved into smiles. The workers, stowing away the coins he handed them, smiled too.

"Better come along with us, master," one of them said. "We've missed enough already. You too, young sir!"

"Later," Amerigo promised. "Go on, and I'll follow you."

They went out, Uncle Giovanni and his late enemies, arm in arm and eager for the show. Amerigo looked after them with a smile.

The smile faded as he unrolled his star map. The light was better here. He could see where he had inked in Polaris, the North Star, and the Great and Little Dippers. They were easy to find and locate in their proper places. He wished again that he could be sure about the Archer.

He went to the door and looked up. The air was hazy with smoke and with dust kicked up by dancing feet. The stars seemed farther away, smaller and not so brilliant. They would be there tomorrow night, blazing away over the hilltop. As Bernardo had said, they were always there.

The stars would always be there. He could hunt for the Archer from the hilltop tomorrow night, and the night after. The festival would be over then. And it is not every night that one has a chance to see a bear dance.

Amerigo Vespucci rolled up his star map and put it away carefully in a safe place. Then, whistling a merry dance tune, he went off to the fair.

In the Cloister

WITH the end of summer, Amerigo and his brother went back to their home in Florence.

The Vespuccis lived in a substantial mansion near the river. The stately chambers, beamed in carved oak, were handsomely decorated and richly furnished. The house had its own family chapel, with a resident priest. This priest, Father Umberto, also acted as tutor to the four boys.

Amerigo was the third son, born in March,

1451. There were two older brothers, Antonio and Girolamo. Bernardo was the youngest.

The parents were Stagio and Elisabetta Vespucci. Master Stagio was a notary, a sort of lawyer whose practice was confined to business contracts. He found plenty to do, for Florence was a business city and proud of it.

The chief business was the manufacture and export of luxury items. Florentine leather goods, beautifully worked and stamped in gold, were in demand all over Europe. The city's dyers and weavers turned dull sheep's wool into glowing rich cloth fit for a king. Florentine goldsmiths were called the best in the world.

Italy at this time was not a united kingdom, but a collection of city states. Each had its own government. Florence was ruled by the powerful Medici family.

The Medicis were businessmen as well as politicians. The great banking house of Medici had branches in several European countries. Medici money backed the building of ships, the outfitting of trading expeditions, and every sort of enterprise from which a profit might be made.

The profits flowed back to them in an endless golden tide.

Amerigo's family did not pretend to compete with the Medicis in wealth or importance. The Vespuccis were one of the "good" families, prosperous and respected, but not especially prominent. Only two members of it had attained distinction in their own right.

These were the two city uncles, one of whom was actually a cousin. The cousin, Guido Antonio Vespucci, was a diplomat in the service of the Medicis. Giorgio Antonio Vespucci, brother to Amerigo's father, was a learned priest, famous for his scholarship. He was Prior of the monastery of San Marco.

It was Uncle Giorgio who had awakened Amerigo's interest in the stars. As soon as he came back from the country, he hurried off to show his uncle the star map.

"I'm afraid it's full of mistakes," he said apologetically. "It's so hard to be sure about the constellations. I think the ancients must have had better eyes than I have, to see all those pictures in the way the stars are grouped. Archers and fishes and goats! I'd never have recognized them if it hadn't been for the drawings in my book."

His uncle smiled. "I don't suppose the pictures were any plainer to the ancients, Amerigo. But it is a convenient way of naming the star groups for study. When one scholar says 'Sagittarius' to another, they both know which constellation is meant. That's what names are for. If your father says 'my son,' I don't know which of his four boys he means. But if he says 'Antonio,' or 'Amerigo,' then there can be no mistake. So you see how useful it is for each to have a name."

The boy's eyes sparkled. "I never thought of that before, but of course it's true. Two people could hardly talk together about anything, unless things had names. Oh, Uncle, how wise you are! I wish— Oh, I do wish I could hope ever to know as much as you do! But I'd have to become a monk for that, wouldn't I? And I don't want to spend all my life behind monastery walls."

"No?" Giorgio Antonio leaned back on the marble bench, smiling down into the young face beside him. It was very quiet in the monastery

garden, with the bees humming in the oleander blossoms and the faint sound of chanting from the chapel. "You do not find this a pleasant place, my boy?"

"Oh, I love San Marco," the boy said eagerly. "And of course I know that to be a real scholar one must join a religious order. Out in the world, men don't have time to read all the books, and study the stars, and talk with other learned men. But—but— Well, it isn't very exciting, is it? Of course at your age, sir, I suppose you don't care about excitement. Oh, I'm sorry!" He broke off, blushing furiously. "I didn't mean that you are really *old*, Uncle."

His uncle laughed, but it was a kindly laugh.

"At least I'm not so old that I can't remember how one feels at twelve, Amerigo. The world is all bright and shining new; a place where wonderful things are happening. You want to travel about and see what is to be seen."

He paused, and Amerigo nodded. That was *exactly* how he felt.

"And yet," Uncle Giorgio went on thoughtfully, "you do feel the call to learning. You want to know, as well as to see."

Again Amerigo nodded. It almost seemed that Uncle Giorgio had power to read his very thoughts.

"Well, the problem is not too difficult," his uncle said gently. "You have six or eight years ahead of you to complete your education. You must make those years count. Into them you must crowd all the learning your head can hold."

"Yes, yes, that's what I want to do, Uncle. But I don't know how to go about it. Father expects me to follow my older brothers at the University of Pisa. But a student's life there— well, honestly, I can't see that Antonio and Girolamo are learning so very much. They talk about fighting duels, and taking part in poetry contests and drinking matches. It seems such a waste of time, when there's so much real knowledge to be gained."

His uncle shook his head. "You are an unusual boy, Amerigo. I've always said so. You have the scholar's bent, and yet there's something of the man of action in you, too, or I'm sadly mistaken. Well, we must think what is best to be done for you. I'll have a talk with your father."

"Will you, Uncle? He'll do whatever you say. I'm only a third son, you know, so I'm not very important. So long as Antonio follows him as a lawyer, he doesn't really care what the rest of us do. Do you think," he asked shyly, "that he'd let me come to you for all my lessons? You're already teaching me natural philosophy once a week. If I could come to you every day, instead of going to the University— Oh, I'd like that best of all!"

"You would? But I'm a hard master, Amerigo. You know that. There'd be no student skylarking under me. You'd have to put in longer hours over your Latin and mathematics than you've ever done with Father Umberto."

Amerigo flushed. "I suppose Father Umberto has told you that I waste my time drawing maps in class. But it's because I've already learned as much as he can teach me, Uncle. And when I ask questions he can't answer, he gets so cross. With you, it would be different. There's no question *you* couldn't answer. I'd work, Uncle— Oh, I promise you I'd work harder than any pupil you've ever had. If only you'd let me come! I know Father would agree, if you asked him."

"We'll see. There's the bell for evening prayer, my son, and I must leave you now."

Uncle Giorgio rose and gathered his robes about him. He was an impressive figure, tall and stately, with his calm eyes and gaunt scholar's face.

Affectionately he patted Amerigo's shoulder. "Don't lose sleep over your future, boy. With the good God's help, all will be arranged for the best."

One week later the arrangements were made. Amerigo was to leave his home and come to live at San Marco, where he would be constantly under his uncle's stern eye. Feast days were to be spent at home, and the summer holidays at Peretola. But school time must be devoted entirely to intensive study.

Latin and Greek, Christian theology, algebra, geometry, penmanship, and Italian literature were among the subjects he must learn. But most important of all was what we now call science. They called it natural philosophy, then. Under this title were grouped astronomy, physics, chemistry, and geography.

The "science" of that day rested upon the teachings of Aristotle and Ptolemy. Any first-year high school student today knows far more of real science than the wisest men of Vespucci's time. But he himself would one day correct some of the world's false beliefs and add important truths to the world's knowledge.

However, that was far in the future. For the

present, he went happily about his studies, soaking up learning as a sponge soaks up water.

His father did not interfere. In the Italian scheme of life, only the eldest son was of any importance. Antonio would inherit the estates and become head of the family when their father died. The younger sons would have to make their own way in the world.

Amerigo continued his studies with Uncle Giorgio far past the age when most boys were ready to leave school. There was so much to learn!

His uncle took him with him on a visit to Rome. Along the way, they stayed at various monasteries, where he met his uncle's scholarly friends. Amerigo saw for himself the sort of life led by learned monks. The old man never urged his favorite nephew to enter the religious life, but Amerigo could not help knowing that it was his uncle's dearest wish.

There is reason to think that he himself gave it serious consideration. It was not until he was twenty-seven years old that he took his final decision.

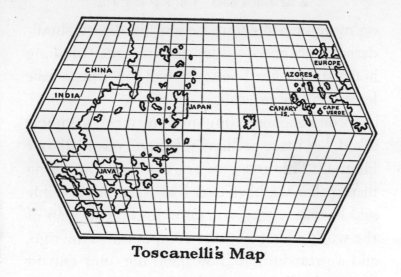

Toscanelli's Map

Amerigo the Businessman

"COME in, my boy, come in."

Uncle Giorgio laid aside his pen and looked up as Amerigo entered the study. He thought, and not for the first time, how handsome this nephew of his had grown. The curling brown hair waved around a thin, thoughtful face lighted by glowing dark eyes. Amerigo was of no more than medium height, but broad-shouldered and narrow-hipped. In spite of long hours spent over books, he had the lithe, active look of a young athlete.

"You have something to show me?" the uncle asked. "A map, perhaps? Master Toscanelli, our librarian, tells me you are the most promising map-maker we have ever had at San Marco. He said he was letting you copy his famous map of the world. That is a rare compliment, Amerigo, and a great honor. Toscanelli does not entrust his precious map to many hands."

"I know. I finished it this morning, Uncle. It fascinated me so that I could not leave it by day or by night. The Maestro is pleased with my copy, I think, although as you know he says little. But it is not the map I want to show you."

"No? Then what? For you are certainly carrying a document of some sort. Is it something I should see?"

If you will be so good," Amerigo answered slowly. "It is a letter from Father's cousin— Uncle Guido, as we boys call him. He has a plan for my future. I thought I should tell you what it is, and ask your advice."

Uncle Giorgio sighed. "I know what it is, Amerigo. Guido Antonio has already laid his plan before your father and me. We all agreed that it is high time you decided upon your life work."

"Yes, sir," Amerigo said respectfully. "I, too, agree to that."

"Yes. I have hoped— Ah, well, you know my hopes. When you were twelve, you told me the life of the cloister would not suit you. Not exciting enough, I think you said. But you are older now, and you have had years to sample the monastic life. It seems to me that it has suited you very well."

"As a student, yes," Amerigo answered. "I shall never forget what I have learned here. And I shall never be grateful enough for your time and patience, Uncle. But— Oh, I don't want to hurt you, sir. And you mustn't think it's a matter of weak faith. I shall always be a loyal son of the Church, whatever I do with my life. I— This is hard to say. I'm ashamed to say it. It may be that my heart is set on worldly things. But I cannot bring myself to be a monk, Uncle."

"Well, well, there is no shame in that," the old

man said gently. "The religious life is not for everyone. God may be served in the world as well as in the cloister. As I know you will seek to serve Him always, Amerigo. If you are certain that you feel no call, I shall not urge you."

"Then you do understand?" Amerigo's voice was warm with relief and gratitude. "I hoped you would. And do you think— Would you advise me about Uncle Guido's letter? He is going to France, on a mission for the Medicis. He would take me as his secretary. To see Paris—" He groped for words, and then they came pouring out. "You don't know how I have yearned to travel, Uncle. Just think, I have never been out of Italy. And Uncle Guido goes everywhere. To Spain, and the Netherlands, and even to the East. If he finds me useful, he may even take me when he goes to Constantinople!"

His voice grew very earnest. "It is my dream, Uncle. It has always been my dream. To go, to see, to know! This world is so wide and wonderful, and I know only our little corner of it. Except for Rome, of course. You took me there. And I can never be done thanking you for it. And now—"

"And now Guido Antonio offers you longer journeys, to farther places. Yes, my lad, I see well enough where your heart is."

The old man sighed, and then smiled his gentle smile.

"Ah, well, we are all as the good God made us. If He gave you this love of far places, be sure that He did it for His own divine purpose. Your father and I have talked of Guido's offer, Amerigo. If you choose to accept it, you will have our blessing."

The matter was soon settled. A few weeks later, in early spring, Amerigo joined Uncle Guido's cavalcade and set out for France.

Nearly two hundred persons made up the party. Guido Antonio Vespucci was an important man, representing the Medici government of Florence, and he traveled in state. There were several clerks and secretaries besides Amerigo. Each had his personal servant to attend to his wardrobe and serve him at table. There were cooks and hostlers and baggage-handlers, and a company of soldier guards. Blacksmiths kept the horses properly shod, and armorers kept the weapons sharp and the armor in good repair.

They moved at a leisurely pace, stopping in the larger towns, where lavish entertainment was offered. There were banquets and tournaments and "courts of song" for their amusement. Twenty-four-year-old Amerigo, stalwart and handsome in blue velvet and silver armor, played his part and enjoyed every minute of it.

It was all very different from the quiet student's life he had known so long. And indeed, his worldly Uncle Guido was very different from the saintly, scholarly Giorgio. Under his teaching, Amerigo learned to move with ease in high society, to chat amusingly, and to pay pretty compliments where they were expected.

He learned other things, too. This was, after all, a business trip. The people of the towns they visited raised or manufactured products from which a profit could be made. It was to the Medici interest that such products go to Florence, instead of to Pisa or Venice. Watching Guido's bargaining, keeping his accounts and copying out his contracts, Amerigo received his education as a businessman.

It was much the same in Paris. Court life was very gay, and the Vespuccis were cordially received into it. But on a hunting trip with the English ambassador, Guido was quite likely to conclude a deal for the purchase of English tin, which he might resell to the Portuguese the very next day. All the important nations had representatives in Paris, making it very convenient for Guido to deal with them.

Amerigo learned commerce as eagerly as he had learned Latin and the sciences. All knowledge delighted him for its own sake. Uncle Guido praised him as the very model of a rising young businessman. He was good-natured and courteous, always willing to see the other's side, and anxious to make sure that both parties benefited from any arrangement he proposed.

The Medicis were always on the lookout for young men of this type. Uncle Guido sent them glowing accounts of his nephew. So it was that when Amerigo returned to Florence, two years later, it was to take his first job as man of business for two Medici sons.

The boys belonged to a younger branch of the family, cousins to the mighty Lorenzo the Magnificent. The elder boy, Lorenzo di Pier Francesco de' Medici, was twenty, and his brother Giovanni seventeen. They had inherited great wealth on the death of their father, but were too inexperienced to manage the estate themselves.

Amerigo took over full responsibility. On their behalf he bought and sold wine, grain, woolen cloth, sheets and towels, silver knives and spoons, tapestry, carpets, and glass goblets. He arranged shipping space for goods to be sent abroad, and kept accounts of money spent and received. As Lorenzo grew older, Amerigo taught his young employer all the business practices that he himself had learned from Uncle Guido.

It was a crowded, exciting life. The best thing about it was the endless travel it involved. The Medicis employed resident agents in all the important cities. Amerigo's duties included supervision of these foreign branches.

He traveled in comfort, for he was handsomely paid. Often, in Rome or in Barcelona, he took time out to visit the monasteries and discuss the latest writings on scientific matters. This was an interest which never flagged, even when he was busiest with buying and selling.

His father died soon after his return to Florence. There were houses and lands, but not much money, for the elder Vespucci had spent his income as fast as it came in. Everything went to the eldest son, Antonio, now married and a lawyer as his father had been. Antonio took the widowed mother into his own home.

The other brothers were not doing too well. Girolamo had gone to the island of Malta and joined a religious order. All we know of him is from the begging letters he wrote Amerigo, pleading for funds to help his brotherhood. Bernardo was working for a wool manufacturer, who did not find him very competent. He too wrote often to Amerigo, asking for money.

Besides helping his brothers, Amerigo also had to do something for the country uncles. Antonio had sold the Peretola estate, leaving them without a home. Until their deaths, the two shiftless old men lived entirely on Amerigo's bounty.

He answered all these calls for money willingly and generously. He was fond of all his relatives, although Uncle Giorgio was always dearest to him. But in his last years in Florence, he saw little of his family. Lorenzo di Pier Francesco de' Medici was becoming one of the city's keenest businessmen. He gave his chief agent little time to attend to personal affairs.

In 1489, when he had been with the Medicis for seven years, his employer sent him on a mission to Spain. The agent at Seville was suspected of being either lazy or dishonest, or both. Amerigo was to find out why the Seville business was being mishandled, and, if necessary, choose a new representative there.

Amerigo went to Seville, where he found that the Medicis' agent was far from lazy. He was doing a thriving business, and putting most of the proceeds into his own pocket. Amerigo promptly discharged him and began looking around for someone to take his place.

The man he chose, Gianetto Berardi, was a prosperous businessman, engaged chiefly in the outfitting of ships. He was not interested in becoming an employee of the Medicis.

Amerigo tactfully proposed a partnership instead. Florence exported sail-cloth and rope, products important in the shipping business. The Medicis would supply Berardi with these and other goods. In return they would buy all the Spanish horses and Toledo sword blades that Berardi could send them. It was a profitable arrangement on both sides. Berardi gladly accepted the offer.

Amerigo's first Spanish visit was brief. But the business grew amazingly under Berardi's capable management. The Seville branch became so important that the Medicis thought they should have a full-time representative there.

Amerigo liked Seville, and he liked Berardi. Two years later, in 1491, he went to Spain to live.

Admiral of the Ocean Sea

AMERIGO bent over his accounts in the Seville warehouse, too absorbed to note the clatter of hoofs on the cobbled street outside. A moment later, his clerk threw open the office door with a flourish.

"The Very Magnificent Lord Don Cristóbal Colón!" he announced breathlessly.

Amerigo pushed aside his papers and rose, bowing low.

"This is a great honor, Your Grace," he said. "I regret that my partner, Berardi, is not here to greet you. As I told your messenger, he is ill at home. But I hope that I may have the pleasure of serving you. Will you be seated?"

Keen hawk eyes swept his face. "You are Señor Vespucci, I believe? Yes, Berardi has spoken of you."

He took the armchair the servant pushed forward, throwing aside his gold-embroidered cloak to reveal a handsome doublet of crimson velvet.

The Spaniards called him Cristóbal Colón. In his Italian birthplace, Genoa, he was Cristoforo Colombo. But English-speaking nations know him best by the Latin form of his name, Christopher Columbus.

Under any name, he was a magnificent figure. He was then forty-two years old, tall and deep-chested, with a head that reminded admirers of a Roman senator's. His hair, once red, had turned snowy white in the long years that he sought

in vain for permission to explore a sea route to India.

Those years had ended triumphantly with the success of his first voyage. The King and Queen of Spain had heaped honors upon him. He had passed through Seville on his way to the court, heading a colorful procession of knights and sailors, with his Indian captives and parrots and nets full of strange fruits.

Vespucci, absent on a business trip to Florence, had missed the parade. Berardi had furnished some of the supplies for the first voyage, going down to Palos to see to it. He and Columbus were well acquainted, but this was Vespucci's first meeting with the Lord Admiral of the Ocean Sea.

He remembered very well his partner's description of Columbus before he set sail.

"A shabby adventurer in a threadbare coat," Berardi had described him. "Not a gentleman born—as you know, his father was a poor weaver of Genoa. But very anxious to rise in the world. And he has the manner for it. If he succeeds, he will make the grandest grandee Spain has ever known."

The prophecy came back to Vespucci now. No one would have dreamed that his visitor was "not a gentleman born." The Admiral wore his fine clothes as if he had never worn any other. His bearing was courteous, but a little haughty, as Spanish noblemen considered it proper to be.

The haughtiness melted quickly at Vespucci's next words.

"And I have heard of you, Don Cristóbal—yes, long before I came to Spain. I was working in the library at San Marco when my master, Dr. Toscanelli, ordered me to make a copy of his world map. It was wanted, he said, for a young sailor who had written a request for it. He was much impressed by the young man's interest in sailing west to reach India."

Columbus leaned forward, his eyes shining. "You *knew* Toscanelli, Señor Vespucci? You actually studied under him at San Marco? Oh, what a privilege! I would have given my right hand to have that honor. But at the time," he added ruefully, "I was living in Portugal, too poor even to afford the journey to Florence. His map caused me a little trouble there, too. I was accused of stealing it from the King of Portugal. No one would believe that the great Dr. Toscanelli had sent another copy to an unknown sailor. But enough of my affairs. Tell me more of the Maestro. Did he really think well of me?"

"Indeed he did," Vespucci answered. "Your letter told him frankly that you were a self-educated man. He was amazed at how much you had taught yourself by reading and thinking. He said he knew university graduates who still believed the earth to be flat, as the common people do."

Columbus sighed. "I myself have met such men—learned scholars in Latin and Greek, but woefully weak in geography. It is true that geography is not a subject to appeal to every man. But it has always been my passion."

"And mine," Vespucci said enthusiastically. "I was permitted to make a copy of the Maestro's map for myself. It is a wonderful document."

"Wonderful indeed! Only a genius could have devised it."

They fell into eager talk about the famous Toscanelli world map. Dr. Toscanelli, librarian of the San Marco monastery where Amerigo had studied, was considered the world's greatest geographer. He was dead now, but no one had yet risen to surpass him.

The Toscanelli map showed the Eastern lands: India and China and Japan. It was largely a work of the Maestro's imagination, since neither he nor any European of his day had ever been there. But it showed those lands on the opposite side of an earth that was shaped like a globe. If you thought about it, as Christopher Columbus had, it was plain that they could be reached by traveling west as well as east.

No one from Europe traveled to the Orient from any direction. The overland eastern route was guarded by the Turks, who permitted no passage. The Turks themselves traded with the East, shipping Chinese silks and Indian pearls and spices to western Europe.

By these products, Europeans knew that the Oriental countries existed. They knew that one Italian, Marco Polo, had visited them nearly two centuries ago, and returned to tell the tale. They knew that, according to Marco Polo, Japan was a collection of islands, and China and India located on a continent called Asia.

And that was about all they did know. The geography of the East had the same fascination that science fiction has today. People speculated on life in Asia as they speculate now about life on Mars. So far, only Columbus had been bold enough to seek a way to the fabled lands.

It seemed that he had succeeded. Neither he

nor anyone else doubted that his first voyage, which ended in the Caribbean islands, actually reached the coast of Asia.

It was true that he had seen no cities and palaces such as Marco Polo described. This could be explained in two ways. It might be that the cities were farther in the interior. Or it could be true, as many scholars believed, that Marco Polo was simply a liar, who invented the whole marvelous tale.

At any rate, Columbus had found Asia; everyone was certain of that. He had come home to report to Their Majesties, and now he was going back again. It was about his new expedition that he had come to Seville. Presently he and Amerigo dropped their discussion of the Toscanelli map and turned to practical matters.

"We will hope that my partner is soon well again," Amerigo remarked. "In the meantime, I shall be happy to assist you. You will require supplies for how many ships and men?"

"Seventeen ships," Columbus answered proudly. "These will be big vessels and well equipped. Nothing like the three miserable little caravels of my first expedition. And as for men,

I propose to take at least twelve hundred. Perhaps more. That astonishes you, Señor Vespucci? But you see, this is not a voyage of exploration, as the first one was. I sailed last year to find the Indies. I have found them. Now it remains to set up a Spanish colony there. I shall need workmen to clear the forests and build a town. The natives will be used for the hard labor, but there must be skilled men to direct them."

"You can depend upon the natives to labor willingly?" Vespucci asked.

"I think so. They seemed a harmless, timid people who did whatever we asked. However, they told us tales of warlike Indians on other islands. To guard against any trouble, His Highness the King is giving me a company of soldiers." Columbus smiled. "Our royal master is a very practical man, Señor Vespucci. He is most anxious to see the gold and pearls and spices of the Indies flowing toward Spain. His gracious lady the Queen considers another matter more important."

"Yes? And what could be more important than a flood of new wealth in this direction?"

"The saving of souls," Columbus answered

solemnly. "Her Catholic Majesty is particularly concerned with the conversion of these poor heathen. She is choosing at least five missionary priests to go with us. Their duty will be to explain the gospel to the islanders and bring them into the true faith. Indeed, she herself is supplying us with furnishings for a church, which she commands us to build first of all."

"A very pious action," Vespucci approved. "I had no idea that your expedition was to be on so large a scale, Don Cristóbal. It will take a little time to assemble all that you will need. But we will do our best."

Luckily, Berardi recovered in time to lend a hand. His firm was by no means the only one concerned. They found one ship; the others were supplied from other sources. But Berardi and Vespucci did round up most of the food supplies for the seventeen vessels. There were flour and biscuits, salt meat, wine, oil, and vinegar, and barrels and barrels of pickles. Pickles were believed to prevent scurvy. No wise captain sailed without plentiful supplies of them.

By mid-September all was complete. The Grand Fleet sailed on September 25, 1493.

The partners went down to Cádiz to see the departure.

It was a gorgeous spectacle. Seventeen proud ships, their snowy new sails gaily painted with the royal arms, decked in flags, brass cannon gleaming in the autumn sunlight.

Columbus and his officers, who had gone for a final Mass at a near-by church, filed down to the docks between lines of cheering spectators. On the wharf he paused to bid farewell to his friends and well-wishers. Amerigo had shaken his hand and turned to give place to others when a voice hailed him.

It was the Admiral's second in command, a young Spanish nobleman named Alonso de Hojeda. He and Amerigo had become good friends during the preparations.

"Don Amerigo!" he called now. "Do you not envy me? You go back to your counting house, while we set off on the road to adventure. You should be with us, my friend."

"Me?" Amerigo laughed. "I'd be very little use, I'm afraid. I'm no sailor, except on paper. Yes, I know I drew up some of the sailing-charts you will use. But map-making in the quiet of my

study is a very different thing from map-using on the high seas."

"Well, perhaps we can change your mind some day. There's the Admiral beckoning me, and I must say farewell."

"Farewell, Alonso, and God go with you."

Amerigo wrung his friend's hand and turned away, a smile playing about his lips. It was all very well for young Hojeda to go a-venturing. But for a settled businessman, forty-one years old and used to soft living, it was unthinkable.

The Admiral Is in Trouble

THANKS, Hojeda, no more." Amerigo
smiled at his host across the table. "That
was an excellent dinner, my friend. So good indeed that I suspect a purpose behind it. Come
now, explain this mystery. Why have you invited me here, with no other guest, and fed me
so royally? Am I right in thinking you want
something from me?"

"You always see through me," Hojeda admitted. "Yes, I do have a favor to ask. A great favor. Don't say no until you've heard me out." He hesitated, and then went on: "As you know, I am sailing to the Indies again in the spring. I want you to come with me."

Amerigo laughed. "Still determined to make a sailor of me? I told you—when was it? Nearly six years ago. Yes, I told you then that I prefer my study to the high seas."

"I know. But I'm hoping to persuade you this time. I need you, my friend. This mission on which the King is sending me—it's a delicate one. There's no one but you I could trust to help me."

Vespucci looked surprised. "Delicate? It seemed very simple to me. Their Majesties want to know more about the riches they can count on from the new colony. Isn't that your mission?"

"It is supposed to be. And you could be useful there. As a businessman, you could judge the extent and value of the pearl fisheries, for instance. Columbus reports a rich supply, but he sends home very small quantities. Also, you could look into the matter of gold and spices, of which we do not see as much as Their Majesties had expected."

"That is not strange," Vespucci commented. "No doubt the Admiral has his difficulties in securing these precious things from the natives."

"The Admiral certainly has his difficulties," Hojeda answered gravely. "And they are not with pearlfishers alone."

"No? Explain yourself, Alonso."

"I'll try. I told you my mission is a delicate one. Its real purpose is to investigate the complaints against the Admiral. The Spanish colonists write that his rule as royal governor is intolerable. They say he is harsh and cruel, punishing with instant death any man who dares to disagree with him. They say—"

"And I say they lie," Vespucci interrupted hotly. "You know as well as I do that these reports are inspired by jealousy and spite. Why do you repeat them to me, the Admiral's friend?"

"I repeat them because you *are* his friend," Hojeda answered. "He needs his friends now, Amerigo. His enemies are many, and they are strong. Not all of them are in the colony.

There are those at court who want to see him discredited. After all, he is an Italian, a foreigner. We have Spanish nobles who would like very well to replace him as governor of the Indies."

Hojeda sighed and went on. "I am the Admiral's friend, too. I served under him, and I know his greatness. If I could, I would refuse this assignment. But I am under Their Majesties' orders. I must go, and see if there is any ground for these charges. And I want you to come with me."

"Why?" Vespucci asked bluntly. "What good could I do?"

"If the charges are true, you can do nothing," Hojeda admitted. "But if they turn out to be false, as we both expect, then you can smooth things over with the Admiral. He is bound to be angry with me for making the inquiry. But you can explain why it had to be made, and—well, just smooth things over," he repeated lamely.

Vespucci looked thoughtful. The proud Admiral was known to have a hot temper. Hojeda meant well, but he was young and not too tactful. Yes, there was certainly need for an older, more experienced man to put the investigation in its proper light.

"If I did go," he said hesitantly, "I would take no part in your inquiries. That must be understood."

"Oh, certainly. Yours will be a friendly visit, that's all. You will be there to value the pearls, and to advise which spices would be most welcome in the European markets. That is the excuse for the voyage. With any luck at all, we can make it appear that it is the only reason."

"Very well." Vespucci nodded. "My business affairs here are in good shape. I can trust my manager to carry on without me for a few months. You have persuaded me, Alonso. When do we start?"

"Early in May." Hojeda did not try to hide his delight. "It will be a small expedition; only four vessels. I'll make you captain of my flagship."

Amerigo shook his head. "I'm no ship captain, Hojeda, and well you know it. No, I'll come as a pilot, nothing more. My study of the stars has taught me the principles of navigation, and I'm very good with sailing-charts on land.

It remains to be seen what I make of them at sea. There will, I trust, be other pilots to set me right if I go wrong."

"There'll be plenty of pilots," Hojeda answered cheerfully. "Juan de la Cosa, the greatest of them all, is going with me. But I'll be surprised if you aren't able to tell him a thing or two. Now let's get down to our plans. Have you any friends you'd like to bring?"

"Only a cabin boy," Vespucci said with a smile. "My brother Antonio writes from Florence that his third son is wild to go to sea. He might as well make his first voyage under my eye. His father calls young Giovanni a strong, intelligent lad. He should be able to make himself useful. I'll see that he does."

They left harbor on May 16, 1499. The little fleet sailed down the coast of Africa until they reached the Cape Verde islands, where they parted company. Hojeda with two ships headed due west, toward the Spanish settlement on Haiti, which was then called Hispaniola. Vespucci struck out southwestward, on a line that no explorer had yet taken.

The splitting up was Vespucci's idea. Hojeda

was off to investigate the situation in the colony. Vespucci, determined to have no part in it, decided to be absent while Hojeda made his inquiries, and turn up later when it was all over.

With time to kill, he decided that he might as well do some exploring on his own. So he took his two ships in the new direction.

Amerigo the Explorer

THE new voyage began as a pleasant, un-eventful one, with good weather and fa-voring winds. The ships were plentifully sup-plied with food and fresh water. They were as comfortable as their builder had known how to make them, although life aboard had its hard-ships.

There was one small cabin, which Vespucci shared with the captain and his officers. The seamen slept on deck, wrapped in their woolen cloaks. Meals were cooked over an iron firebox set on the open deck. A boy carried hot soup, fish, and beans to his masters in the cabin. The men ate their portions on deck, squatting wherever they chose.

There was little to keep the sailors busy while the fair weather held. Every morning the decks were scrubbed and the brass fittings polished. Then the captain assembled all hands on deck for morning prayer. The crew was divided into two watches, each on duty for four-hour stretches. The off-watch men whiled away the time with cards or dice, or in story-telling and singing.

There were three or four young boys aboard, learning the sailor's trade. The boys took turns at the half-hour glass, the ship's "clock." The real clocks of that time would not work at sea, because of the tossing about by the waves.

It was the boy's job to watch while the sand trickled slowly from the upper glass into the lower one. The last grain meant that half an hour had passed. The boy must keep a sharp eye for that second, and instantly turn the glass upside down to start all over. Sometimes he sang as he watched, to a cheerful little tune:

> *"The first glass empties*
> *As the second filleth;*
> *The sand shall flow*
> *So long as God willeth."*

One of the boys who took his turn at the half-hour glass was Amerigo's nephew, Giovanni. His uncle had warned him that he must expect no favors. He must take his place with the other ship boys, keeping the cabin clean, serving the officers' food, washing their shirts, and doing whatever odd jobs there were.

Giovanni cheerfully accepted his duties. He was thrilled to be at sea, and eager to do everything he could to repay his uncle for bringing him. Amerigo soon found that he had a real interest in navigation. He taught the boy to use the mariner's compass and the quadrant, and predicted that he would make a good pilot one day. Amerigo should know, for he had found that he himself was a very good pilot indeed.

He was so good that he had not hesitated to

make himself responsible for the course of the two ships. Juan de la Cosa, the master pilot, had gone with Hojeda, assuring Amerigo that he had no need of any supervision. Amerigo's long study of the stars and his mastery of mathematics had made him as skilled as de la Cosa himself.

Young Giovanni watched and learned as his uncle worked out the ship's position in latitude and longitude. He followed Amerigo's notes and shared his excitement as the little ship slowly approached the equator.

"Will our stars go with us after we cross the equator?" he asked one night.

Amerigo smiled. "I thought I had explained all that, Giovanni. I see I must repeat it in simpler language. Listen, then. The stars we know are those of the northern hemisphere. Polaris, the North Star, stands steadfast above the North Pole. The earth's bulge is greatest at the equator. As we fall below it, that bulge will hide the northern horizon we know. Our northern constellations will seem to sink lower in the sky, and to change their shapes. Can you see why that would be?"

"No, I can't," Giovanni answered frankly. "I don't think it's much use expecting me to know why the stars look different past the equator, Uncle. I'll be satisfied if you'll just tell me what will be different about them."

Amerigo laughed. "Your ignorance is refreshing, my boy. I'd far rather have you confess ignorance than pretend to understand when you don't. Very well. Let's just say that the stars we know will seem lower, and farther away. It may be that we will lose them altogether. But to make up for that, we'll see new stars not visible in the northern hemisphere."

"New stars? What are they called?"

"Who knows?" Amerigo's voice quickened to enthusiasm. "A sky full of strange stars, never seen or named by white men. And we shall be the first white men to look upon them; perhaps to give them their names. But no, that would be presumptuous. We will report what we see to the learned astronomers at home, and they will choose the names. But we shall *see* the southern stars, Giovanni; the first of our race to do so. Oh, what a wonderful thing that is! That sight alone will make our voyage worth while."

"It may be the Indians have named their stars," Giovanni ventured. "If there are any Indians past the equator. We don't even know if there's any land there, do we?"

"No, but we'll find out," his uncle answered gaily. "Asia is a big country, bigger than anyone dreamed. So far the Admiral has found only a small part of it. If Marco Polo spoke the truth —and I've always believed that he did—there must be a part of Asia where the cities are, and the kings in their golden palaces. Perhaps we may come upon that part."

"Oh, Uncle, if only we could! That would be the finest sight in the world."

"Finer than the southern stars? I don't think so," Amerigo answered. "Kings I have seen, and palaces, too. And always I shall love stars best. But I can't deny that I find this search for strange lands more exciting than I had expected. Perhaps I should have gone exploring long ago, as Hojeda urged me."

"Yes, it's too bad you put it off until you were so old," the boy said innocently.

Vespucci gave him a wry smile. Long ago he had made such a remark to Uncle Giorgio.

Where had they gone, those years since he was twelve? He had not thought of himself as growing old. Yet now, at forty-eight, he must seem as old to Giovanni as Uncle Giorgio had seemed to him.

He roused himself to say briskly: "Well, be thankful you're getting an earlier start, my boy. And now off to bed with you. I have work to do."

But he did no work after Giovanni left him. The little cabin was hot and stuffy. He left his charts and went out on deck.

Picking his way among the sleeping sailors, he approached the rail. The little ship rode easily on the gentle waves, crested with silver in the starlight. Up forward, the helmsman held the course, with the hour-glass boy beside him for company. All around lay the starlit sky and the lonely sea.

The boy was right, Amerigo told himself. He had waited too long. Why had he wasted his youthful years over ledgers and bills of lading? Why had he thought that it was enough to study geography from books?

His mind went back to the twelve-year-old

Amerigo who had thought Uncle Giorgio so old. He could hear his own boyish voice, breaking with eagerness, declaring that he must go, and see, and learn at first hand of the world's wonders. Where had they gone, the years between? Somehow, somewhere, he had taken another road. Was it too late to turn back and find the right one?

He stretched, feeling the muscles ripple under his skin. He had never felt stronger, or younger. The rough shipboard life had hardened him to discomfort. He had not missed his soft bed and his luxurious home. Too late? It was not too late. No, not even at the advanced age of forty-eight.

Swiftly he began to plan. He was sole head of the Seville business now, for his partner Berardi had died a few years ago. At that time, Amerigo had bought out the Medici interest, so that he was free to act as he chose. Although no longer his employer, Lorenzo di Pier Francesco de' Medici remained a warm friend. Amerigo was sure he could count on his approval of his new career.

Just what that career was to be he did not

yet know. Something to do with the sea, and
the stars, and the strange new world that lay
about him in these strange waters. Something
that would add to the world's store of knowledge, as Aristotle and Ptolemy had added to it
in their time.

This had been his boyhood dream. This was
what Uncle Giorgio had hoped for him. And
now, in what of life remained to him, he would
set about it.

The Tree-walled Coast

WEARIED from his long vigil, Amerigo slept late next morning. He was roused by Giovanni tugging excitedly at his sleeve.

"Uncle, Uncle, wake up! The watchman has sighted land ahead. Any minute now we'll see the golden palaces."

Vespucci tumbled from his bunk and hurried on deck. All the men not on duty were clustered at the rail, straining their eyes toward the south.

Only the watchman, high on the mainmast, could see anything but tossing waters.

A brisk breeze sent the ship steadily onward. By mid-morning it was plain to all; a dark smudge that turned into a thicket of tall trees.

As they drew nearer, they saw that there was no beach. The forest came right down to the water's edge. They sailed a little way along the coast, but could find no landing-place.

Vespucci turned to the captain. Hojeda had given him command of the expedition, but he was careful not to hurt the captain's pride by issuing orders. Instead, he offered his wishes as friendly advice.

"I think it would be well to anchor here and take to the boats, Captain. Perhaps we can find a cove or beach that will accommodate the ship."

The captain nodded and gave the order. Two boats, with six men in each, were made ready. The captain took his place in one, and Vespucci in the other.

Giovanni looked pleadingly at his uncle, but he knew better than to ask to go along. Only stout oarsmen were needed. There was no room for young sightseers.

All day long the two boats followed the edge of the land, trying for an opening among the trees. There was none. The giant trees stood with their roots in the water, with not a grain of sand to be seen between them. Low-growing bushes filled in the chinks between them, and a network of tough vines laced one to another.

The most striking thing about the coast was the fragrance. The trees were masses of bright-green leaves, hung with brightly colored flowers and lush ripe fruits. They gave off a heavenly odor like nothing the men had smelled before. It was all very beautiful, and the smell was de-lightful, but it offered no welcome. No place could they find a spot where a landing could be made.

The sun was setting when they gave up the search and returned to the ship. They lay at anchor all night, and sailed on when daylight came.

Although they did not know it, they were skirting the upper, or northern, coast of Brazil. They were the first Europeans to set eyes upon it. And when at last the dense green barrier broke, it revealed the wide mouth of the Amazon River.

They knew only that they had found an entrance at last. And very disappointing it was. The open bits were tiny islands, swampy and bare, surrounded by water too shallow for a ship to approach. Along the river's nearer bank, as far as the eye could see, there was only that blank green wall.

Again the ship anchored, and the boats were ordered out. This time most of the ship's company took to the boats, leaving only a few men on watch. It was hoped that the boats could surely find some sort of landing-space upstream.

It was another disappointment. They spent days, rowing nearly a hundred miles up the Amazon, to find it still lined with thick jungle. Once or twice, looking across the treetops, they could see smoke rising. This seemed to show that there were inhabitants farther inland. But no one came near them, and they could find no way to reach the smoke. The first name for the Amazon, the one Amerigo gave it on his map, was "River of Hidden Fires."

Shut in from the sea breezes, they found the sweet scent almost overpowering. The treetops were alive with unknown birds of brilliant colors. "An earthly paradise," the sailors called the river country, and doubled their efforts to go ashore. But the leafy gates of paradise were closed against them. Try as they would, they could find no spot where a man could set his foot.

After four days of it, they returned to the ship and sailed on. The skipper and his men were bitterly disappointed. But Vespucci remained as cheerful as ever.

"I thought surely we'd find a way to get to the palaces," Giovanni sighed. "The men hoped we'd come across gold or pearls, but I don't care about that. All I want is to see the palaces. Don't you, Uncle?"

Amerigo shook his head. "All I want is to see what there is to be seen. We saw a mighty river, broader than any river of Europe, I should think. We saw trees and fruits and birds such as we had never seen before. Now we know what is here. When we come to another place, we shall see what is there. I am content to sail on, and let the wonders unroll as God wills it."

"But what if we *never* find the palaces? Oh, I don't think I could bear that."

Vespucci smiled. "You build disappointment for yourself, my boy. A wise man expects nothing, and rejoices to welcome what comes. To see, to *know*—that is all that matters. And now come out on deck, and I will show you something I promised you. This morning we crossed the line of the equator. We go now to observe the southern stars."

They blazed overhead, the Southern Cross, as yet unnamed, and a host of strange constellations. Their old friend, the North Star, lay low upon the horizon. "A few more nights, and we shall lose him entirely," Vespucci remarked. "But have no fear. He will be waiting when we turn north again."

They followed the Brazilian coastline for two weeks more before they were forced to turn back. This was at the point where Brazil juts farthest eastward. Past this point, the coast turns sharply to the south. Strong ocean currents met them here, forcing them out to sea. They had found no place to land, and their food and water were running low.

On Vespucci's advice, the ships turned about and retraced their course. The currents, which had been against them, favored them in their new direction. They made good time, and sped past their first landfall just one month after their first glimpse of it.

Heading northwestward now, they came at last to an island with a bay which offered a good harbor. For the first time in long weary weeks, the Vespucci party was able to go ashore. For the first time, they made the acquaintance of the natives of the New World.

Every Day Is Friday

THE copper-skinned, naked island people took to the woods as the visitors rowed ashore. When the ship's boats reached land, they found the sandy beach deserted.

Vespucci beckoned to Giovanni. "You brought the bells, as I told you?"

"Oh, yes, Uncle." The boy lugged forward a leather bag of tiny metal bells, each hung on a leather thong. "But how can I give them to the people? There's no one here."

"Take them to the edge of the woods. Keep them ringing as you go. String them up on the nearest branches, and come away."

The sailors squatted on the sand to wait. Giovanni did his errand and came back to join them. Soon they saw a brown arm part the branches, and one of the little bells disappeared. The visitors waited patiently.

"Don't move," Vespucci cautioned them. "Columbus told me that the Indians are timid as wild hares. Talk and laugh among yourselves as though you did not see them. They should soon overcome their fears."

It did not take long. One man stole cautiously out of the woods, to make his choice among the bells. Soon others followed. The sailors pretended not to notice as a steady tinkling drew nearer.

A crowd of about twenty men came to huddle near them in a fearful little group. They were led by a tall old savage, evidently the chief. Vespucci did not look up until the old man spoke. He talked for several minutes, with many gestures. The white men could not understand the words, but the tone was friendly.

When he had finished, Vespucci rose and bowed.

"O King, if you are a king," he said in Spanish, "greetings! Greetings in the name of our most High and Mighty Sovereigns, our noble lord King Ferdinand and our liege lady Queen Isabella. Greetings from the Kingdom of Castile, and of Aragón, united under our glorious Sovereigns. Greetings from the city of Seville, and of Barcelona, and of—"

The speech went on and on. There was no sense to it, and no need of sense, since the chief understood not a word. But politeness demanded that the visitor respond to one long speech with another equally long.

Giovanni's attention wandered. Farther along the beach, he saw something that looked out of place here. Quietly he stole over to examine it.

The thing was a substantial wooden cross, raised on a heavy block of wood. And on the base, the arms of Spain had been carved. Under them was a Latin inscription.

Painfully the boy tried to spell out the words. His Latin was not so good as he could wish, and the letters were poorly cut. But he could make out the names of the King and Queen, and at the end the signature of Christopher Columbus.

Giovanni walked around the cross. On the opposite side of the base a large inscription stood out bold and clear. *Isla de la Trinidad*. Island of the Trinity. Without doubt, the Admiral had visited this place and given it this name.

He was so interested that he did not notice the speechmaking was over. He was startled to hear his uncle's voice behind him.

"Come, my boy, the chief has invited us to a feast. You must— In the name of heaven, what have you found?"

"See for yourself, Uncle. We aren't the discoverers of this island, after all. The Admiral has been here before us."

"The island of Trinidad—yes, it appears on the Lord Admiral's map. But I am sure he placed it much farther west. Well, this is good news. It means that we are nearer than I'd thought to the Gulf of Pearls, which Columbus also discovered. This will give me an opportunity to do as Hojeda asked, and see the source of the pearls for myself. His Majesty will be glad to know how large the oyster beds are, and whether most of the pearls are of good quality."

"Aren't we going to do any more exploring, then?" Giovanni asked. "I liked it better when we found places that no one else had seen."

"No doubt you did. But you must remember that I have duties to perform. Now come along to the feast. Oh, and a word of warning, my boy. The day is Friday, on which we eat no meat. See that you touch none if it is offered to you."

"But of course, Uncle! I never eat meat on Friday; you know that. Only—how can it be Friday? Surely yesterday was Monday?"

"Today is Friday," his uncle said firmly. "And tomorrow is Friday, and the next day also, if we remain so long. I have said so to the men, and I say it to you. This is Friday. Every day on Trinidad is Friday. See that you do not forget it."

"How odd! But I suppose it's something to do with the strange stars. I'll never know all you know about *them*, Uncle. But I'll remember. Every day on Trinidad is Friday."

They spent three days on Trinidad, each one

marked by a feast with the chief. As it happened, no meat was served at any meal. Instead, there were several kinds of fish, nicely browned over hot coals and served on long, green leaves. Other leaf dishes held a kind of cereal mush, highly spiced and peppered. There were fruits and berries, unfamiliar but delicious, and some nasty-tasting palm wine.

The sailors spent their time cutting firewood and loading fresh water and fruits and vegetables. The natives were friendly and helpful. They produced a few pearls, and pointed westward to show where they came from. On the third day the ships hoisted sail and headed for Paria, the Gulf of Pearls.

Giovanni looked back as the island receded.

"I suppose that was the first king," he sighed. "I must say he was a mighty poor one. Not only did he have no royal robes—he didn't even have a pair of pantaloons! And his palace was nothing but a grass hut. I like the hammock he gave me, though. I'm going to sling it up and sleep in it every night. Yes, he was a nice king, even if he is so poor. And his island is nice, too. But there's one thing I can't understand, Uncle. Why is it always Friday on that island?"

A sailor standing near by laughed uproariously.

"Listen to the little innocent! My mates and I guessed right away when you told us that tale, master. You didn't have to tell us that these bloody heathen—"

"Get about your work, Jorge," Vespucci said curtly. He beckoned Giovanni over to the rail, where they could talk undisturbed.

"This may be a shock to you, Giovanni, but it is as well you should know. These islanders have their customs which—well, which fill us with horror. You must remember they are not Christians yet. Some day, when the good fathers have brought the gospel to them, they will give up their sinful ways."

"What ways, Uncle? Like going around naked and showing no shame?"

"That, among other things," Amerigo said slowly. "They are guilty of worse sins than nakedness, Giovanni. The people of Trinidad are cannibals. Eaters of human flesh."

Giovanni clutched at the rail, his cheeks suddenly white.

"I—I think I'm going to be sick," he said faintly. "That kindly old man—he gave me my hammock! Oh, it can't be true, Uncle."

"It is true," Vespucci answered sadly. "I suspected it, from something I remembered from the Lord Admiral's reports. He said that some of the Indians—not all—were cannibals. I could not know if it was true in Trinidad. But I warned you and the men to eat only fish, just in case. And it is true. I learned to talk to the chief fairly well in the sign language. He admitted it without shame, but said it only happened in wartime, when they had many captives. Praise God that we arrived in a time of peace. Now," he added firmly, "we'll say no more about it. Remember that Her Majesty has taken a vow to see to the conversion of all the Indians. Holy Church will deal with the crime in God's good time. So put it out of your mind."

This was easier said than done. For the rest of the voyage, Giovanni was unable to feel at ease with the natives they met. Some were cannibal tribes and some were not. But wherever they went ashore, Giovanni took no chances with the food. For him, every day was Friday.

A short run brought them to the Gulf of Pearls, where unexpected news awaited them. It appeared that Hojeda and de la Cosa had visited the Pearl Gulf a month before. They had traded for a considerable quantity of pearls and some gold ornaments.

On second thought, Vespucci did not find this news so surprising. No doubt Hojeda had decided to do a little trading before visiting Haiti, as though that were the real reason for his voyage. He had not come too far out of his way, for Haiti lay to the northwest of the Pearl

Gulf. Probably Hojeda had reached Haiti by this time and begun his inquiry.

Vespucci was still determined not to arrive in the colony until the investigation was over. He spent a few days in the Gulf, trading bells and knives for pearls. He watched the divers at work, and guessed at the size of the pearl-oyster beds. This was the sort of information the King would expect from him.

Leaving the Gulf, he sailed westward along the northern coast of South America. To him, of course, it was the coast of Asia. No one had yet realized that this was a new continent. Columbus never realized it. To the day of his death, he would maintain that he had found an unexplored part of India. Vespucci was to learn the truth, but not on this voyage.

Westward they sailed, with frequent visits ashore. The land here was swampy, so the natives had built their huts on stilts to keep them out of the wet. Seeing the huts rising out of the water, with boats plying between them, Vespucci was reminded of Venice in Italy. He named the land Venezuela, "Little Venice."

At first they met only friendly natives. But

off the Venezuelan coast they encountered war-like tribes who resisted their landing with spears and arrows. There was bitter fighting, and bloodshed and death on both sides.

Vespucci had not come to the New World to fight a war. He was a man of peace, willing and anxious to make friends with the natives. It pleased him to find that they were a brave people, not afraid to defend their homes. But he had no way of making them understand that he meant them no harm. After the last battle, in which several of his men were badly wounded, he decided to go no further, but to make for Haiti.

Downfall of the Admiral

THE Vespucci expedition reached Haiti, called Hispaniola by the Spanish, in late September. Hojeda, they learned, had already arrived there, and had spent some weeks in talking to the dissatisfied colonists. As tactfully as he could, Hojeda had laid their complaints before Columbus, and asked for his side of the story.

The Admiral was furious. He declared that he represented the Spanish Crown here, and would answer no questions from his inferiors. His colonists were an insolent, worthless lot, plotting to overthrow him and seize the rule for themselves. He demanded that Hojeda take certain of them home in chains. "Otherwise," he threatened, "I shall be obliged to hang them as an example to the others."

All this Hojeda reported to Vespucci. "He'll do it, too. Indeed, I am assured that he has already hanged several men who displeased him. He says it is necessary to maintain discipline."

"But what are the rights of it?" Vespucci asked. "*Are* they plotting against him? It may be that he has good reason for his severity."

"Perhaps." Hojeda shrugged. "It is my private opinion that the Admiral, great man though he is, is not well fitted to be a governor. He holds himself more royal than the King, and expects everyone to bow down to him. These Spaniards don't like that, especially since he is a foreigner."

"But he does represent the King here. His Majesty himself appointed him. The colonists know that."

"They know it, but they don't like it." Hojeda sighed. "If you ask me, there is right on both sides. Fortunately, I am not here to judge. My business is to gather the facts and put them before Their Majesties. I have invited the colonists to put their complaints in writing. I asked the same thing of the Admiral, but he haughtily refused. Perhaps if you talked to him—"

Vespucci shook his head. "I told you from the beginning, Hojeda, that I would have no part in this. As things are, I am embarrassed to be here. Well, you have chosen the only course. Gather their stories and lay them before the King. Tell him yourself what the Admiral has told you. And then let His Majesty decide."

As Vespucci had said, it was a most embarrassing position for him. He did the best he could. There was one meeting with Columbus, a friendly one in which no mention was made of trouble with the colonists. Columbus was too proud to bring up the subject, and his friend pretended to know nothing. It was an uneasy visit, and Vespucci was glad of an excuse to leave the island without repeating it.

Columbus himself had mentioned the near-by Bahama Islands.

"There are hundreds of them, clustered together like flies on a ripe melon," he remarked. "I explored them a bit, but found no gold or pearls to make it worth while to go farther. However, they do have some fine trees that would make excellent ship's timber."

"Indeed?" Vespucci looked interested. "My ships are going to need extensive repairs before we begin the long voyage home. We need new masts for one, and deck planking for another. Perhaps I could have it done in these islands you speak of."

It could have been done as well on Haiti, and both men knew it. But, under the circumstances, it was a relief to both of them to part company as soon as possible.

A few days later, Hojeda told Vespucci he was ready to go home. He had gathered a big sheaf of complaints against Columbus.

"Their Majesties must do with it what they will," he said wearily. "I want no more to do with it. Will you be ready to sail when I do?"

Vespucci shook his head. "I'm making for the Bahama Islands, of which the Admiral told me. He says there are tall, straight trees there, suitable for masts, and good wood for planking. As you know, my ships are not in the best of shape. It may take some time to repair them properly. Don't wait for me. I'll follow you home to Spain in my own time."

"I see." Hojeda gave him a sour smile. "You're determined not to be associated with my mission, aren't you? Well, I can't blame you. I'll be glad to see the last of it myself."

Hojeda sailed directly for Spain, where he laid the complaints before Their Majesties. The King at once sent Chief Justice Bobadilla to the colony, with full power to deal with the situation.

It did not take the Chief Justice long to decide. The first sight that met his eyes, as he entered port, was a gallows from which hung the bodies of twelve Spaniards. Their only crime, their friends told the Chief Justice, was to protest the Admiral's tyranny.

Bobadilla looked no farther. He arrested Columbus and threw him into jail, fettered hand and foot. He himself moved into the Admiral's house, seized his personal property, and took up rule as governor. He sent Columbus home for trial, with a stack of testimony taken from the colonists.

Once safely at sea, the ship's captain offered to strike off the fetters. Columbus refused. "Since I am chained by Their Majesties' orders," he said bitterly, "I will wear the manacles until they themselves release me."

They released him as soon as he was brought before them. Queen Isabella is said to have wept at the pitiful sight. But although he was quickly freed, his post of governor was not restored to him.

The plain truth was that he had not done well at it. Columbus had many talents, but the governing of men was not one of them. His intolerant pride would not let him admit that he could ever be in the wrong. Only his enemies were to blame for his misfortunes. His day of glory was ended, and the "grandest grandee in Spain" was sadly fallen from his high estate. He could not even know, for his comfort, that his name would live forever in the bright pages of history.

The Chief Justice must have arrived in Haiti

while Vespucci was still in the Bahamas. He knew nothing of it, for he did not return to the colony. His party spent several months in the pleasant semi-tropical islands, making repairs to the two ships and exploring the islands themselves. Then they turned homeward, reaching Spain in June of the year 1500. The voyage had taken thirteen months.

Once at home, Vespucci could catch up with the news. Besides the Admiral's sad story, there was other news from beyond the seas. A Portuguese expedition under Vasco da Gama had sailed down the coast of Africa, around the Cape of Good Hope, and into the Indian Ocean. Crossing it, da Gama reached India, the real India, on its west coast.

He found India much as Marco Polo had described it—a civilized Oriental land, with cities and with riches to trade. It was quite unlike the "India" which Columbus stoutly maintained he had found by sailing west. There was a good deal of argument among learned men as to why this should be. Da Gama, approaching from the west, reached India's western coast. It was presumed that Columbus, sailing west, had sighted eastern

India. But why should the same continent have civilization on one side and naked savagery on the other? It was all very perplexing. It perplexed Vespucci most of all.

He found the discussion raging when he went to court to report his voyage to Their Majesties. They were more interested in his report on the pearl fisheries than in the mysterious tree-walled coast he had not been able to penetrate. However, they did agree to give him ships for another expedition. No date was set, and he went back to Seville to await their pleasure.

He had scarcely reached home when a messenger came to summon him to Lisbon. King Manuel of Portugal was anxious to talk to the man who had earned Juan de la Cosa's praise as a master navigator. Portugal was sending out one expedition after another, and needed all the good navigators she could get.

Vespucci felt immediately at home in Lisbon. The Portuguese royal family had always taken a personal interest in exploration. He found that King Manuel could discuss maps and navigation as intelligently as any pilot. He was delighted to see that the young King valued knowledge for

its own sake. When Vespucci described the endless tree-lined coast, he found instant sympathy for his hope to follow it to its end.

"As you know," the King remarked, "we are at present directing our expeditions eastward rather than west. But it may be I could find you a few ships to explore your tree-bound coast."

Regretfully Vespucci declined the offer, explaining that Their Majesties of Spain were planning such an expedition for him. He did not feel free to enter into any other arrangement at this time.

"Very well," the King agreed. "I will not press you. But if at any time you are free, I hope you will consider a voyage on behalf of my country."

Vespucci thanked him and went back to Seville. There, some personal matters claimed his attention. He must carry out his plan and dispose of his business interests, so that he could give all his time to exploring.

It was not hard to find a syndicate of Spanish merchants anxious to buy him out. Among them was a gentleman named Fernando Cerezo. The negotiations, in the leisurely Spanish manner, involved a good deal of time and several meetings. In the course of them, Cerezo invited Vespucci to dinner at his home. There his hostess was Doña María, Cerezo's sister.

She was years younger than Vespucci, and very lovely. He lost his heart to her at their first meeting. So far as is known, this was his first romance. His hard work and constant traveling left him little time for social life. When he did have a bit of leisure, he preferred to spend it in study. Perhaps the young ladies he met found him too serious for their taste. Certainly he had remained a bachelor into middle age, and there is no mention of any woman in his life until he met Doña María.

He wooed and won her as impetuously as any young man could have done. In the same month, her brother became part owner of the old firm and María became his wife.

The marriage was a very happy one. There were no children, but the nephew Giovanni came to take a son's place in their household. Amerigo's brother Antonio had more sons than he knew what to do with. It was the old story over again. Amerigo's father, blessed with four boys, willingly gave up one of them to Uncle Giorgio, and then to Uncle Guido. As Uncle Giorgio had done, Amerigo took up his own nephew's education. Giovanni became an expert navigator, and so good a map-maker that in time the King appointed him map-maker to the crown.

The days and months went happily by. Only one thing bothered Vespucci. Nothing was being done about his new expedition. He talked with Bishop Fonseca, a power at the court, and learned that Their Majesties were losing enthusiasm for the New World. The Columbus affair had distressed them. Their colony on Haiti was giving them more trouble than profit. They were not inclined to spend money on a new expedition unless its leader could guarantee to bring back a wealth of pearls and gold.

Vespucci could guarantee nothing of the sort. He wanted to follow his tree-walled coast to its end. He could not even guarantee that he would be able to land on it, much less bring back any treasures it might hold. If indeed it held any. The only treasure he wanted to seek was knowledge. And this, it appeared, was a treasure for which Their Spanish Majesties had no use.

His thoughts went back to another King who had felt differently. Manuel of Portugal had said nothing of treasure. It was coming his way now from the real India, thanks to da Gama's venture. His Majesty could afford to finance an expedition which offered no certainty of profit. And he had said he would be glad to have Vespucci at any time.

Amerigo talked to the Bishop, and went to Lisbon, and came back to talk with him again. The good Bishop saw no reason why he should not change flags if he chose. He was an Italian, not bound to serve Spain exclusively. Bishop Fonseca had a little confidential chat at court, and reported to Vespucci that Their Majesties would not be offended if he relieved them of their promise.

So on May 13, 1501, Vespucci began his voyage in the service of Portugal.

Under a New Flag

VESPUCCI was delighted with the Portuguese ships and their captains and crews. The vessels were larger and faster than the Spanish ships, and easier to handle. The sailors were tough, experienced seamen. Of the three captains, two had made the long run around Africa to the East Indies. They were all accustomed to hardships, and careless of danger.

Again, as on the Spanish voyage, Amerigo was master pilot, not captain. His authority, by his own choice, was limited to "directional command." This meant that he would decide the expedition's course. The ships would sail wherever he directed them. In everything else, the three captains kept full authority on their three ships. Amerigo had two or three pilots under him, and young Giovanni as pilot apprentice.

The little fleet ran down the coast of Africa, and stopped at the African port of Dakar before striking out into the open Atlantic. In Dakar harbor they found two Portuguese ships, homeward bound. They were returning from India with what their captain boasted was the richest cargo ever brought to Europe. He invited Vespucci aboard to see for himself.

The ship was heavily loaded with all the riches commonly associated with Asia. There were grass baskets filled with cinnamon, ginger, pepper, cloves, camphor, opium, and other drugs. Gaily lacquered chests held exquisite porcelain dishes. There were also several coffers of diamonds and rubies.

"You traded beads and bells for these precious things?" Vespucci asked wonderingly.

The captain stared. "Certainly not. We paid

for them in sound Portuguese gold. Let me tell you those Orientals are no fools. They drive as hard a bargain as any Europeans."

That night Vespucci entertained the ships' officers at dinner. Among them was an Egyptian named Gaspar, who had acted as interpreter. Vespucci had a private talk with him after dinner.

"I can't reconcile it," he declared. "You have seen the people of India on their west coast. They wear clothes; they manufacture beautiful objects. But on the east coast, it is all so different. Admiral Columbus found nothing but naked savages. I, myself, skirting the northern edge of this same continent, saw no sign of human life. I could not even force my way ashore for the trees. Why should these things be?"

"It puzzles me, too," Gaspar answered. "On our way out, we were driven off course by high seas. We too saw a tree-lined coast with no inhabitants. Our leader, Captain Cabral, claimed the land for Portugal, although he had to drive his cross in a bit of sand no larger than a tablecloth."

"You saw the tree-lined coast?" Amerigo's interest quickened. "That is where I am bound. Tell me of your experiences there."

There was little to tell. As soon as the wind changed, the Portuguese had struck out eastward again, coming at last to the tip of Africa and the Indian Ocean.

Vespucci resumed his voyage a few days later. Fair weather changed to foul as soon as they left the land behind. For sixty-four days the three ships wallowed in mountainous waves, swept by howling winds, lashed by furious rain. It took all of Amerigo's skill to hold the fleet on the course he had laid out. Some days they made no progress at all. On others they barely crawled. But little by little they crept toward the Brazilian coast.

At last there came a morning when Vespucci wakened to early sunlight slanting across the cabin floor. The ship was speeding smoothly along, without the rolling and pitching which had made the voyage so wretched until now.

He went on deck, to find Giovanni just turning out of his blankets. A junior-grade pilot was not important enough to share the cabin with the senior officers. The boy rubbed his eyes and blinked in the bright sunshine.

"Good morning, Uncle. Look at that sea— as calm as a lake. No wonder I overslept. It was the first night in weeks that I didn't roll from one side of the deck to the other." He sniffed inquiringly. "What do I smell? Something sweet, spicy—or do I imagine it?"

"I hope not," his uncle said delightedly. "Your nose is younger than mine, and sharper. You must remember the smell when we were here before. The wind carried it out to us before we could see land. Sniff hard, now. My old nose tells me nothing. But does yours get just a whiff of the tree-lined coast?"

Giovanni's eyes grew big with excitement. "Uncle, I *do!* Just now, it was more than a whiff. But the breeze has shifted, and it's gone. I can't be mistaken, though. I did smell it, our own long-lost tree-lined coast!"

They made land before dark. It was not quite their "own" coast, for they were below the point where they had turned back the first time. It was even better, however, for here the thick trees grew farther inland, leaving narrow sandy beaches.

They sailed southward a bit, and found anchorage in the mouth of a small river. They decided to lie at anchor overnight, and go ashore when day came.

After supper, Amerigo got out his old map. On it, the coastline stopped short where they had turned back. That had been at latitude six degrees south. Their present position, as he worked it out, was eight degrees south.

"Not too great a gap," he remarked to Giovanni, who was watching him. "We won't go back to fill it in now. I'm far more interested in seeing what lies to the south."

"What do you think lies there?" Giovanni asked.

His uncle smiled. "I don't know. But I'm afraid you will be disappointed of your kings and palaces, my boy."

"Oh, Uncle! Why do you say that?"

"I have done a lot of thinking and figuring since we left Dakar," Vespucci answered slowly. "I've concluded that this globe on which we live is a far larger globe than anyone believed.

Yes, even Ptolemy must be wrong about its size. Toscanelli must be wrong. I think there is room on this great globe for vast continents of whose very existence no scholar ever dreamed. I think"—his voice strengthened—"I am sure that we are on the rim of such an unknown continent now. Not Asia. No more Asia than it is Europe or Africa. Its peoples are different, its fruits, and its animal life. It cannot be the continent Marco Polo saw!"

"But what is it then?" The boy's voice sounded frightened.

"A new world," his uncle answered solemnly. "Or, I should say, a new quarter of the world. Perhaps—who knows—a new *half*, for we can only guess at its size. Oh, the wonder of it! From the time of our first parents, mankind has lived in half a world, and thought it the whole."

"And I suppose the Indians thought their half was the whole," Giovanni said. "They didn't know anything about us."

"Not Indians, boy. The true Indians, who trade with the Turks and now with the Portuguese—they know of us, as we know of them. But in this new world there is a new people.

What they should be called I do not know. But they are no more Indians than they are Spaniards."

"Whatever they are, they are cannibals, and I'm afraid of them," Giovanni remarked with a shudder. "If there aren't any kings and palaces in this land, then I don't care if the trees keep us from going ashore. But I suppose you'd be disappointed if we couldn't, Uncle. You don't seem to *mind* cannibals!"

His uncle laughed and tweaked his ear.

"There you go, borrowing trouble as always! We don't know that the people of this coast are cannibals. We do not even know as yet that there are people here. Let us wait and see before we condemn them. And in the meantime, I have a task for you. You have your calendar of saints?"

"Oh, yes, Uncle. I look at it each morning after prayers. Today is St. Augustine's day."

"Good. This little river where we are anchored must appear on our map, and it must have a name. I think it would be well to call it Río de San Agustín. St. Augustine's River."

"I think so too," Giovanni agreed. "It will

show that the discoverers of this new land are Christian men. But what is the task you have for me, Uncle?"

"Finding names for the spots we visit. When we come to a place important enough to name, you will suggest a suitable one. If it is a saint's day, you will tell me, and we will call it after the good saint. If it is not, I'll depend upon you to think of a new name. Do you like this task?"

"Indeed I do," Giovanni cried. "It's a great honor for me. To think that when I'm dead and gone, schoolboys will study a map with the names I put there! I'll be very, very careful. You can be certain I'll never give you the wrong saint's name."

Vespucci smiled. "Then I leave it in your hands. We'll have the ship's carpenter make a wooden cross, and you may letter it yourself with the words Río de San Agustín. Tomorrow we'll find a spot to drive it into the river bank."

The spot they found was a very small clearing among the great trees. The growth was not so thick here, but it was still difficult to penetrate inland. After a few days, they sailed on to the south.

As they proceeded, they found that the forest grew steadily thinner. Many little rivers and bays offered anchorage. Giovanni marked every stopping place on the new map—for St. Michael, St. Francis, St. Sebastian, and many others. The crosses claimed the land for Portugal.

On the day after Halloween, All Saints' Day, they reached a fair-sized bay with open land around it. They named it All Saints' Bay and went ashore.

After planting their cross, a party of sailors went into the forest for firewood. Some of the men began to fish. A feast ashore would be a welcome change from shipboard fare.

The firewood seekers came out of the woods more quickly than they had entered them.

"There's a heathen village in there," one of them reported. "Just two or three houses, but big—as big as our houses at home. We saw some women cleaning fish, and there were children playing around."

"Did they see you?" Vespucci asked.

"Oh no, sir. We ran away quick and quiet. There were a lot of men lounging in the shade— big, fearful-looking fellows with fishbones stuck in their lips. We'd better get away from here, master. We'd be no match for that lot."

"Nonsense." Vespucci got to his feet, settling his sword at his side. "If they want to fight, our weapons are more than a match for their arrows and darts. But there's no reason for fighting. We have no quarrel with these people. There must be a way to make them understand that."

The ship's captain spoke up.

"We're only one ship's company, Senhor Vespucci. The other two vessels are several leagues behind. I do not think it wise to engage in battle with these savages, whose numbers we cannot know. We must return to our ship and sail on before they discover our presence."

Vespucci's calm eyes surveyed him. "I think not, Senhor Captain. We are here to explore this land. Sooner or later, we must hold parley with the people who live here."

"But if I give the order—" the captain began angrily.

Vespucci broke in politely, but firmly.

"May I remind you, sir, that it is I who give orders as to our course? I ordered that we anchor in this bay. I do not order that we leave it now."

A little murmur of agreement came from a few of the bolder men. One of them spoke out.

"Why should we run away from these shirtless ones? Cold steel beats bows and arrows any day, and we're well armed. You're right, master pilot. I say let's stay and fight it out."

A chorus of voices rose, some supporting the captain, some siding with the man who had spoken. Vespucci waited quietly. Then Giovanni tugged at his sleeve.

"Look, Uncle— They're coming out of the woods. They've heard us, after all. What do we do now?"

The boy's voice was shaking, but he tried hard to seem brave. His uncle laid a reassuring hand on his arm, and turned to the men.

"It's too late to run now. Captain, you will forgive me if I assume authority. I demand that all of you remain quiet, making no threatening gesture unless we are attacked. Giovanni, give me— What do you have? Here, this will do."

He snatched off the boy's cap. It was of knitted wool, gaily striped in red and yellow.

The savages were moving closer now, silent, watchful, but seeming more curious than hostile.

Vespucci popped the cap on his own head and stepped out to meet them.

Three stalwart young warriors stood slightly in the lead. As the seamen had said, they were fearful-looking fellows. Polished fishbones were thrust through their cheeks. In addition, the middle one had a large green stone set in the flesh of his upper lip. Guessing that this was the chief, Vespucci swept off the cap and held it out to him.

"For you, sir, with my compliments," he said, smiling, and with his most courtly bow. "Very useful for keeping off the chill dew of evening. Will you do me the honor to accept it?"

There was a breathless minute while the young chief turned the cap about in his hands, fingering the soft wool. Then slowly, seriously, he put it on his head and turned to his men. They broke into delighted grins and chatter that could only mean admiration.

Vespucci nudged Giovanni. "Run quickly and bring all the trade goods you can find. The little bells, and the beads, and the colored scarves. Hurry!"

As soon as he came back, Giovanni helped

distribute the presents with a lavish hand. The savages accepted them with grunts of pleasure. Most admired of all, however, was the chief's cap. All the sailors had caps of the same sort, but theirs were of dull gray wool. Perhaps it was as well there were no more colored ones, for the chief took it as a special tribute to his rank.

The meeting, which began so dangerously, ended with friendliness all around. The Europeans were taken to the forest village for a mighty feast. Besides vegetables and fruits, they were served shrimps, lobsters, crabs, and some nicely roasted bits of what was undoubtedly meat.

Vespucci noted Giovanni's agonized look as the meat dish was passed to him.

"Rabbit or something of that sort," he whispered. "See the size of the bones, boy! You may eat it without fear. But to set your mind at rest, I'll see what I can learn from the chief."

The young savage was intelligent, and understood Vespucci's sign-language fairly well. Certainly his people ate their enemies captured in war, he declared. Was it not right that evil men should be put to good use? But never, never did they eat their friends. That would be a wicked thing to do.

Giovanni was relieved when his uncle communicated the reply to him.

"All I pray," he said fervently, "is that they remain our friends!"

And friends the tribe remained. The party spent several days in the bay. At the chief's cordial invitation, Vespucci himself went ashore and lived in the principal long house, sleeping in a hammock and going hunting with his new friends. Giovanni and the ship's company were not so daring. They lived aboard ship, but came ashore for hunting and fishing expeditions.

Vespucci kept careful note of all that the natives told him about their way of living. It appeared that they did not farm, or trade, or make even such simple things as clay pottery. Six or eight families lived in a palm-leaf house, bare of any furnishing except hammocks and a few bark mats. The bone and stone ornaments on their faces, he learned, were to frighten their enemies in war. If there was gold under the ground here, they did not know it, for they had never thought of digging. However, they would dig for their white friend if he wished it.

Vespucci did not wish it. In a letter to Lorenzo di Pier Francesco de' Medici on his return, he wrote:

"Because we went solely to make discoveries, and not to seek for any profit, we did not trouble ourselves to search the land or look for any gain."

He did very little trading, and he did not travel far inland. When he returned from the voyage, he brought home facts, not treasure.

The other two ships joined them in a few days, and the new arrivals were given time to rest and relax on land. Then, loaded down with fresh fruits and flowers, the only gifts their native friends had to offer, they sailed out of All Saints' Bay.

A New Name on the Map

A FEW days' sailing brought them to another landing-place, and another friendly tribe. This was repeated several times as they proceeded down the coast. They had no trouble with the natives, but there was little to learn from them, and they did not linger long.

Following the Brazilian coastline south, they came to the point where South America narrows and swings sharply to the west.

At this point a decision had to be made. They had reached the Line of Demarcation, the meridian which divided Spain and Portugal in the western hemisphere. The two countries had agreed a few years before that all land discovered east of that meridian was to be Portugal's; all west of it to belong to Spain.

When the agreement was made, no one knew that any undiscovered land lay on Portugal's side. Columbus's discoveries were all in the Spanish zone. But the eastern coast of Brazil, which Vespucci was now exploring, had so far been east of the Line. Wherever he had gone ashore, he had claimed the land for Portugal. Now, arriving at the Line, he was about to pass into Spanish territory.

The Spaniards had no knowledge of it. But it was their land, by agreement between the two nations, and Vespucci was in the service of Portugal. His ships' captains were in favor of turning back at once. No one wanted to create an international incident by trespassing on Spanish territory.

Vespucci could not bear to turn back. He was already nearer the South Pole than any white man had ever been. He knew that he was exploring a new continent. Did that continent extend all the way to the Pole? Or was there a southern tip with open sea beyond?

Africa had a southern tip, and the Portuguese had found it. By sailing around it, they had reached India from the west. If this new land had such a southern tip, Vespucci could sail around it as da Gama had sailed around Africa. And if he did that, he would find the westward route to India for which Columbus had aimed.

His wishes prevailed, and the expedition continued south. But now they set up no more crosses, claiming the land for Portugal. Instead, Vespucci contented himself with keeping a careful map marked with the names Giovanni chose for him.

Prominent on the map was a mighty river running over silvery sand. They called it by the Bible name of River Jordan. This was later changed to Rio de la Plata, Silver River. The city of Montevideo stands at its mouth, where Vespucci dropped anchor four and a half centuries ago.

February 1, 1502, was St. Julian's day. They

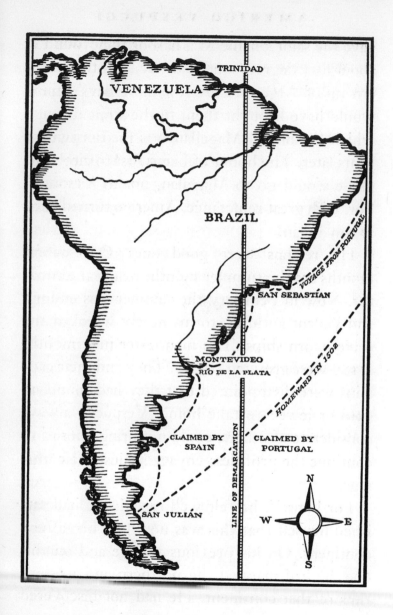

gave the saint's name to a harbor they found at about fifty degrees south latitude, near the southern tip of Argentina. A few more days' sailing would have brought them to the strait through which Ferdinand Magellan was to pass twenty years later. The honor of being first to circle the globe would go to Magellan, not to Vespucci. For, with great reluctance, Amerigo turned back at San Julian.

His reasons were good ones. Our winter months are the summer months below the equator. Now in February the summer was ending, and violent autumn storms nearly wrecked the travel-worn ships. The men, after nine months at sea, were growing restive. They and their captains were disappointed that they had found no gold or jewels to take home. Vespucci, always considerate of others, could not bring himself to continue the profitless voyage against their urgings.

For himself, he felt well repaid. He had satisfied himself that this was not Asia, but a new continent. On his previous voyage and on this one, he had mapped the northern and western rims of that continent. He had not discovered it. Columbus had been before him at the Gulf of Pearls (Venezuela). Captain Cabral of Portugal had set up the first cross on the tree-walled Brazilian coast. Vespucci was not the first man to see the new continent. He was the first man to know that it *was* new.

Besides this knowledge, he had acquired a wealth of information about the people, the plants and animals and climate. He had made some valuable observations of the southern stars, and worked out some new theories of navigation. He would have liked to go farther, but as it was, he had a fine budget of new facts to carry home. With that he contented himself for the present.

The homeward voyage was swift and uneventful. In June 1502, thirteen months after he had set sail, Vespucci reached Lisbon and the end of his Portuguese voyage.

He remained in Portugal long enough to report what concerned that country. The fact that on a Portuguese voyage he had discovered land belonging to Spain was an embarrassment. The two countries, rivals in exploration, liked to keep exploring secrets from each other.

Vespucci related the bare facts of his journey after he entered Spanish waters, and no more. Fuller details, he felt, should properly be communicated to Spain. He was anxious to get back to that country as soon as possible.

There was another reason for his return. He had been obliged to turn back before he reached the tip of the new continent. Portugal had its eastern route to India. But Spain, in spite of what Columbus believed, had not yet reached it by sailing west. If there was a way around the tip of the new continent, it could be done. And Vespucci wanted very badly to do it.

He felt certain that Ferdinand and Isabella would welcome the idea of a new expedition. He hurried to the Spanish court and had his first disappointment. The King was away in Naples, and the Queen was ill. His good friend the Bishop advised him to go home to Seville and wait for a more favorable time.

He went back to Seville, to a warm welcome from his friends there. Business was humming. The Spanish colonies had not yet produced much gold, but they were sending home valuable cargoes of mahogany, dye barks and berries, and

natives to be sold as slaves. The slave trade was
not a great success, for the Indians sickened and
died in the European climate. But in the beginning it was an important part of Spain's over-
seas trade.

The merchants of Seville had organized a
Board of Trade to deal with all this new business. It was natural that they should offer Vespucci a post with them. His old friend Hojeda
was already in the Board's service.

Amerigo had made no money out of his voy-
aging, and he had a wife and adopted son to sup-
port. No doubt María urged him to stay at home
and go back to business. She may have put it on
grounds of health, for her husband was not a
well man.

Vespucci had picked up malaria in the tropics.
He was never able to shake it off. At that time,
European medicine knew no cure for the dis-
ease. He must have seen many cinchona trees
in the sweet-smelling forests of the tree-lined
coast. He had no way of knowing that their
bark would yield quinine, the drug that was to
conquer malaria.

His illness came and went, with periods of

wellbeing between the attacks. He labored faithfully, buying and selling for the Board of Trade. And time went by, with no news of royal approval for a new expedition.

In June 1503, Lorenzo di Pier Francesco de' Medici died in Florence. Vespucci's patron had shown the letters about the two voyages to his friends, who found them intensely interesting. Now that the Medici was dead, the letters became part of his estate. It occurred to someone to publish them.

The whole matter of the publication is wrapped in mystery. Vespucci was not consulted. No one knows who the first publisher was. The slim little volume, issued in August 1504, was printed in Vienna. It was called *Mundus Novus*, New World. The book contained only those Medici letters in which Vespucci described his Portuguese voyages. No mention is made of Spain. But the editor had made some changes, inserting references to other voyages.

Bare as it was, the little book created a sensation. The public clamored to know more of this New World where men lived in a state of nature not unlike the Garden of Eden.

The publishers were happy to oblige. A new and longer work appeared a month later. Its title was *Four Voyages*. It was made up of letters, signed with Vespucci's name, and supposedly written to Piero Soderini, who had succeeded the Medicis as head of the Florentine government.

In *Four Voyages*, the writer told of an expedition for Spain in 1497, on which he reached Central America, Mexico, and Florida. This, if true, would make Vespucci the first European to touch North America. That honor is commonly assigned to John Cabot.

Then followed the Spanish and Portuguese expeditions, with material similar to that of the Medici letters. However, here it was greatly expanded and embroidered. A fourth voyage, said to have been made in 1503, was not given so much space.

The baffling thing about *Four Voyages* is that it may be genuine. Most modern historians, on the available evidence, declare that the Soderini letters are forgeries, concocted by the publishers to make a sensational story. They argue that Vespucci was in business with Berardi at the time of the supposed 1497 voyage, with no thought of going to sea. They find fault with the language of the Soderini letters, saying they are the work of an uneducated man, which Vespucci certainly was not.

On the other hand, a distinguished Latin American, Dr. Germán Arciniegas, has recently written a Vespucci biography in which he accepts the Soderini letters as authentic. He may be right, but the weight of scholarly opinion is still against it. Our standard textbooks and encyclopedias agree that the 1499 voyage was Vespucci's first.

On one point at least there is no dispute. Vespucci himself had nothing to do with the publication of any of the letters, true or false. He was living in Spain, and the books first appeared in Austria and Germany. True or false, they became runaway best sellers. Publishers in France and Italy printed new editions, with fanciful drawings and with wild, badly written anecdotes that appear in none of the Vespucci letters.

These later books were for the ignorant public, who would believe anything. But the first two were taken seriously by scholars. In 1507 a group of learned cartographers met at a French university. They agreed with Vespucci that the land in the western Atlantic was actually a new continent. It needed a name. They had read *Mundus Novus* and *Four Voyages*. One of them, Professor Martin Waldseemüller, suggested that the New World should be called America, for the man who had first realized that it was truly new.

If the name of Columbus was considered, it was passed over. The Admiral, unhappily, had fallen from the high regard in which he had once been held. The professor's suggestion was adopted. The maps they prepared, based on Vespucci's explorations, showed "America" across the southern continent. Its extension to North America came many years later.

Vespucci did not ask for the honor. It is entirely possible that he never even knew of it. He was now a subject of the Spanish King whose western possessions continued to be known as the Indies. Long after his uncle's death, Giovanni was making maps for Spanish sea captains. None of these maps bears the word "America." So firmly did Spain stick to the old name that even now the Caribbean islands are known as the West Indies.

The Last Journey

IN 1507, the year that his name first appeared on the French map, Vespucci was summoned to court.

If he had given any thought to the map, or to the two books bearing his name, those matters were crowded from his mind by the royal command. He had waited on the King's pleasure for five years now. Surely, after this long wait, he was at last to be given his new expedition!

He reached the palace at the time appointed, and was invited to make himself comfortable in the anteroom until the King sent for him.

The anteroom was a luxurious chamber, hung with tapestries whose heavy folds almost shut out the daylight. Groping his way to a chair, Amerigo stumbled over the feet of a man already seated. When he began his apologies, he realized that the man was an old friend.

It was Juan de la Cosa, the pilot who had accompanied Hojeda on the first voyage. He shook Vespucci's hand warmly, and waved to the seat beside him.

"We might as well make ourselves comfortable," he observed. "Royalty is never punctual. And now tell me, how goes it with you, Vespucci? I heard that you were off to the Indies earlier in the year. Have you come to report some new discoveries?"

"None, I'm sorry to say. It was only a short business mission. The Board of Trade wanted to make sure of safe transport for a shipment of gold. I've had no chance of a real voyage of exploration since I returned from Portugal. I'm hoping that His Majesty means to give me a chance now."

"Perhaps." De la Cosa looked doubtful. "Now that the Queen is dead, our lord the King shows little interest in exploration. It was an ill day for us navigators when Her Majesty passed away. I think the blow fell hardest upon our friend Columbus. She was ever his kind patroness. After her death, he lost all hope of restoring his fortunes. Ah, his end was a sad one, God rest his soul!"

"A sad end indeed," Vespucci agreed. "I saw him often before his death last year. You know he had a house in Seville. He was hard-pressed for money, and that last unfortunate voyage crushed what little spirit he had left. Then, too, the pains of rheumatism kept him in constant agony. When last I saw him, he was a feeble, crippled old man, hard to recognize for the Very Magnificent Don Cristóbal. So many of his friends deserted him, too. He felt that very keenly."

"Well, you at least were faithful," de la Cosa commented. "I heard that you interceded for him at court shortly before he died."

Vespucci shook his head. "I tried, but there was nothing I could do. He heard that I was going to court on business for the Board of Trade. He urged me to beg the King to aid him. I had to explain that I was not likely to see His Majesty, since my business was with one of the lesser ministers. I did mention his name wherever I could, but it seems that nothing came of it."

"Ah well, so it goes! The higher one rises in this world, it appears, the lower one falls."

De la Cosa turned his glance to the outer door, where some more visitors were entering. Then he stood up and beckoned them over.

"Vespucci, of course you know Vicente Yáñez Pinzón and Juan Díaz de Solís. What have we here, gentlemen? A convention of pilots? So it would seem. Now, I wonder what our lord the King has in mind for us?"

They were soon to find out. Vespucci had scarcely greeted the two pilots, old acquaintances of earlier days, when the chamberlain bowed them into the King's presence.

Ferdinand of Aragón rose to greet them: a tall, melancholy man with a weary battle-scarred face. Ferdinand was a great soldier, who pre-

ferred the battlefield to the palace. With beautiful, brilliant Isabella gone, he was like a ship
without a rudder.

Vespucci's heart sank at sight of him. The
King, as court gossip had it, was a man with
many troubles. His daughter was insane, and his
son-in-law was plotting to depose him. Anxious
moments and sleepless nights stared out of the
sunken eyes. This was not a man to be fired by a
dream of new—and costly—explorations. Whatever was the reason for this summons, it was not
to give Amerigo the glad news that he might
plunge deeper toward the southern pole.

His guess was right. The King had a less ad-
venturous project on hand. To discuss it, he had
summoned the four leading pilots of his kingdom.

He meant, it appeared, to set up a school of
navigation. Spanish pilots, except for the four
before him, were a slovenly lot, far behind the
Portuguese in knowledge and skill. With trade
to the Indies increasing, too many treasure-
laden ships had been lost through unskilled
handling. They had split on unseen reefs, or

gone down in storms which better navigators could have weathered.

The four men nodded their agreement. It was for this very reason that the Board of Trade had sent Vespucci to pilot an especially valuable ship on the homeward trip. The other three pilots had had similar demands for their services. The proposal of a school to train better pilots met with their full approval.

"Very good," the King said. "It shall be done. Now one matter remains to be settled. Who is to head this school? Each one of you is well qualified to do so. I ask you to put aside petty jealousies, if you have any, and tell me which of you is best suited for the post."

There was a moment of silence. Then Pinzón ventured to ask: "Is it the plan that this school will be held at sea, where the director can see his directions carried out?"

The King frowned. "Certainly not. I am not thinking of a school for beginners, who may still obtain their practical training on shipboard. No, it is the skilled pilots, those who call themselves masters, who will be your pupils. These men, the best of them, are woefully weak in the theories of navigation. They need to know more about reading and making maps. Half of them are unable to take proper soundings and compute the ship's speed with accuracy. They do not pay sufficient attention to the new means of determining longitude which you, Señor Vespucci, have devised for us. On all these matters they must be instructed."

Three of the men exchanged glances. It was de la Cosa who spoke.

"Among us, Your Highness, there can be no doubt. As regards the theory of navigation, Amerigo Vespucci is master of us all."

Vespucci, genuinely startled, protested that he would not dream of holding himself superior to the other three. But they held to their position, and the King accepted it.

"Then I shall name you Pilot Major, Señor Vespucci. Any man desiring a license to pilot Spanish ships will be required to submit to an examination by you. If you find him lacking, you will teach him what he needs to know. If he fails to learn, the license will not be granted."

The others bowed. But Vespucci said firmly:

"If Your Majesty permits me to say so, there must be three exceptions. Nothing would induce me to pass upon the qualifications of Juan de la Cosa, who taught me much that I know. Or of Pinzón, or de Solís, who proved their skill at sea while I was still in the counting house."

"Naturally I excepted these," the King said without hesitation. "But we shall show no such grace to others. Now what do you say, Señor? Have I my new Pilot Major before me?"

Vespucci bowed his acceptance, and the King went on to talk of arrangements. Since Amerigo had a roomy house in Seville, well equipped with navigational instruments, day classes would be held there. A handsome salary was named, with a bonus to be paid by each pupil who successfully passed the examination.

When the interview ended, Vespucci went with his friends to a near-by inn. The toasts they drank loosened their tongues. He learned with wry amusement that their recommendation had not been wholly unselfish. They were seafaring men, accustomed to life on the ocean wave. The thought of spending their days shut up in a classroom filled them with horror.

The prospect did not greatly appeal to Vespucci either, now that he was out of the royal presence. A great honor—oh, yes! But he would far rather have been told that he could take some ships around the new continent and try to find India.

It was hard to give up that dream. His thoughts turned to the King of Portugal, who had seemed so sympathetic to following wherever the pathway led. But it was no use appealing to Manuel now. The Portuguese ships were all needed for the booming India trade. Even if they were not, Portugal could not sponsor an expedition into Spanish waters. And that was where he wanted to go. No, there was nothing to do but accept the appointment and make the best of it.

He went back to Seville, where María's warm approval soothed his hurt. She would never, she declared, know a happy day if he took to the sea again. He himself had admitted that his recent short voyage had been most uncomfortable. Didn't he realize that he was no longer a young man, and that when a man passes fifty he must have his comforts? To say nothing of the fits of chills and fever which came on without warning, leaving him helpless for days on end. How would he like being ill on a heaving, tossing ship, with no wife to smooth his pillow and make him cooling drinks?

And anyway, María concluded finally, no one refused a royal request, which was the same thing as a command. Especially when His Majesty had ordered exactly what a loyal wife would have him order.

So Amerigo set up his school. Once it was well under way, he would not have left it for any ship. It was a difficult task, and one that challenged every ounce of skill and energy he could bring to it. He had never thought of himself as a teacher. Now he found that teaching brought him a rarer pleasure than he had ever known.

It was not easy to win the pilots over. There was a good deal of resentment among experienced men, suddenly called in for examination. But here Vespucci's gift for getting along with people served him well. He was patient, and kind, and genuinely interested in helping each man advance rapidly. A few passed their examination after only five or six lessons. Most of them managed it after a period of coaching. For those who could not, Vespucci took pains to suggest some other occupation better suited to their abilities.

His only assistant was Giovanni, now in his twenties, and an expert map-maker. All new maps and charts were brought to the Vespucci school for approval as new territory was explored. Giovanni checked them, compared them with others, and made master maps for the Spanish fleet. The number of shipwrecks declined sharply. New voyages were undertaken with greater assurance. The setting up of the pilot school was one of the wisest acts of King Ferdinand's reign.

Amerigo had five peaceful, happy years as Pilot Major to the King. Without envy he watched his pilot friends set out on their voyages and come home again. He was saddened when word came that his good friend de la Cosa had been killed by poisoned arrows on the Venezuelan coast. He rejoiced when Pinzón and de Solís added Honduras and Yucatán to Giovanni's growing map.

Besides his work among the pilots, he found time to correspond with scholars all over Europe. Many of them were particularly interested in his observations of the stars below the equator. The stars were his first love, and he found astronomers more congenial than other men of learning. But to the geographers, too, anxious for facts about the strange lands he had seen, he gave freely of his knowledge. He was only following the path laid out by his Uncle Giorgio. "The aim and purpose of a man's life," the saintly old monk had said, "is to add to the world's store of knowledge." Gladly and generously Amerigo made his contribution, as his uncle had done before him.

His health grew worse in the harsh winter of 1512. The time came when classes must be discontinued, for the master lay abed, shivering and burning, too weak to hold a book.

On the afternoon of February 22, 1512, Giovanni roused María. She had watched at the bedside day and night, and was snatching a brief nap. She started up at Giovanni's touch. At sight of his face she broke into wild sobbing. He answered the question she could not ask.

"Not yet. But it is very near. The priest is with him now."

Controlling their tears, the wife and nephew knelt beside the bed as Vespucci received the last sacrament. When it was over, he smiled and stretched out his hands to them. Then, quietly and without fuss, as he had begun all his voyages, Amerigo Vespucci embarked on his last journey.

He would be long dead before the cruel, bitter slanders began. He died beloved, respected, with more fame than he ever asked for. He had asked for so little in life! He never commanded an expedition or sought to rule others. He had no taste for titles or riches. All he wanted was to go, to see, to know. What he knew he gave to the world.

In later years, small-minded men would call him a liar, an impostor, a thief who stole the credit that should have gone to Columbus. He was as good a friend as Christopher Columbus ever had. Never would he have dreamed of claiming the credit another had earned.

He did not discover America. He did not name it. Columbus, the discoverer, is surely

America's father. But Amerigo Vespucci, whose name our country bears, is just as surely its godfather. They were two brave, honorable men, and between them they found the New World and gave it its name. In American hearts, there will always be glory enough for both.

America's father. But Amerigo Vespucci, whose
name too many bears, is not assuredly its godfather. They were two brave, honorable men,
and both of them they found the New World
and gave it its name. To American hearts, there
was room in the glory enough for both.

Authorities Consulted

BOOKS

ARCINIEGAS, GERMÁN. *Amerigo: The Life and Times of Amerigo Vespucci*. New York, Alfred A. Knopf, Incorporated, 1955

MORISON, SAMUEL ELIOT. *Admiral of the Ocean Sea; A Life of Christopher Columbus*. Boston, Little, Brown & Company, 1942

POHL, FREDERICK JULIUS. *Amerigo Vespucci, Pilot Major*. New York, Columbia University Press, 1944

ZWEIG, STEFAN. *Amerigo; A Comedy of Errors in History*. New York, The Viking Press, Incorporated, 1942

ENCYCLOPEDIAS

CATHOLIC ENCYCLOPEDIA. 17 vols. New York, Catholic Encyclopedia Press, 1907-22

AUTHORITIES CONSULTED

COMPTON'S PICTURED ENCYCLOPEDIA AND FACT-INDEX. 15 vols. Chicago, F. E. Compton & Company, 1954

ENCYCLOPAEDIA BRITANNICA. 24 vols. Chicago, Encyclopaedia Britannica, Incorporated, 1954

WORLD BOOK ENCYCLOPEDIA. 18 vols. Chicago, Field Enterprises, Incorporated, 1954

Index

Africa, 53, 90, 98
All Saints' Bay, 106, 113
Amazon River, 69, 70
America, 125, 140
Arciniegas, Germán, 124
Aristotle, 21, 64
Asia, 41, 42, 61, 103, 118
Austria, 124

Bahama Islands, 87, 88, 90
Berardi, Gianetto, 33, 34, 36, 37, 44, 63, 123
Board of Trade, 121, 128, 133
Bobadilla, Chief Justice, 88, 89
Brazil, 60, 71, 100, 114, 115

Cabot, John, 123
Cabral, Captain, 99, 119

Cádiz, 45
Cape Verde, 53
Central America, 123
Cerezo, Ferdinand, 93, 94
Cerezo, María, see Vespucci, María Cerezo de
China, 40, 41
Colombo, Christoforo, see Columbus, Christopher
Colón, Cristóbal, see Columbus, Christopher
Columbus, Christopher: meeting with Vespucci, 35-45, 49-51; as royal governor, 76, 82, 84-90, 95, 99, 119; later life and death, 125, 129, 130, 140, 141
Cosa, Juan de la, 53, 59, 91, 128-35, 138

Da Gama, Vasco, 90
Dakar, 98

Ferdinand, King of Spain,
    37, 43, 44, 88, 91, 95,
    120, 128-35
Florence, 7, 13, 14, 32, 33
Florida, 123
Fonseca, Bishop, 95, 96,
    120
Four Voyages (book), 123,
    125
France, 27, 124

Gaspar, 99, 100
Genoa, 38
Germany, 124
Gulf of Pearls, 76, 79, 81,
    82, 119

Haiti, 53, 81-4, 95
Hispaniola, *see* Haiti
Hojeda, Alonso de, 45, 47,
    48-54, 59, 66, 76, 81, 82,
    87, 88, 121
Honduras, 138

India, 40, 41, 90, 91, 98, 99
Indians, 74-83, 103, 106-12

Isabella, Queen of Spain,
    37, 43, 44, 89, 90, 95,
    120, 129, 132

Japan, 40, 41

Line of Demarcation, 115
Lisbon, 91, 96, 119

Magellan, Ferdinand, 118
Manuel, King of Portugal,
    91, 92, 96, 136
Marco Polo, 41, 42, 61, 90
Medici family, 14, 26, 27,
    30-4, 123
Medici, Lorenzo di Pier
    Francisco de', 30, 31,
    33, 63, 113, 122
Mexico, 123
Montevideo, 116
Mundus Novus (book),
    122, 125

Naples, 120
New World (book), *see*
    Mundus Novus
North America, 125

Palos, 38
Paria, *see* Gulf of Pearls
Paris, 26, 29, 30

INDEX

Peretola, 7, 21

Pinzón, Vicente Yáñez, 130-5, 138

Pisa, University of, 19

Portugal, 91, 96, 116, 119, 136

Ptolemy, 21, 64, 103

Río de la Plata, 116

Río de San Augustín, 104-6

Rome, 22

San Marco monastery, 15, 17, 21, 39, 40

Science, 21

Seville, 33-5, 37, 42, 91-4, 120, 121, 136

Soderini, Piero, 123, 124

Solís, Juan Díaz de, 130-5, 138

South America, 114

Spain, 32, 34, 115, 119-21, 124

St. Francis, 106

St. Julian's Bay, 116, 118

St. Michael, 106

St. Sebastian, 106

Toscanelli, Paolo, 24, 39, 40, 103

Trinidad, Island of, 76

Turks, 41

Umberto, Father, 13, 20

Venezuela, 82, 83, 119

Venice, 82

Vespucci family, 7, 13-15

Vespucci, Amerigo: and the stars, 4-12, 15, 16, 59, 60; born, 13, 14; early life, 4-34; leaves Florence for Spain, 34; first meeting with Columbus, 36-46, 49-51; first voyage, 55, 90; marriage, 94; second voyage, 96-119; with Board of Trade, 121; continent named for, 125; appointed Pilot Major, 134; death, 139

Vespucci, Antonio (brother), 14, 19, 22, 53, 94

Vespucci, Bernardo (brother), 4-7, 13, 14, 32

Vespucci, Elisabetta (mother), 14, 32

INDEX

Vespucci, Georgio Antonio (uncle), 6, 15-23, 32, 61, 62, 64, 95, 139

Vespucci, Giovanni (uncle), 4-11, 32

Vespucci, Giovanni (nephew), 53, 57-61, 65, 66, 70, 71, 74-81, 94, 95, 98, 100-8, 112, 116, 125, 138

Vespucci, Girolamo (brother), 14, 19, 32

Vespucci, Guido Antonio (cousin, called uncle), 24-30, 95

Vespucci, María Cerezo de (wife), 121, 136, 137, 139, 140

Vespucci, Niccolò (uncle), 8, 32

Vespucci, Stagio (father), 14, 19, 22, 32

Vienna, 122

Waldseemüller, Martin, 125

West Indies, 126

Yucatán, 138

A NOTE ON THE

Type

IN WHICH THIS BOOK IS SET

THE TEXT *of this book was set on the Linotype in Janson, a recutting made direct from type cast from the original matrices cut by Anton Janson. Janson, who may have been of Dutch origin, purchased a foundry and was a practicing type-founder in Leipzig between 1660 and 1687. His first specimen sheet was issued in 1675. His successor, Johann Karl Edling, issued a later specimen sheet showing all of Janson's types in 1689. The Janson matrices were later brought to Holland, from whence they were sold in 1720 to the Erhardt foundry of Leipzig. Later acquired by the Drugulin foundry of Leipzig, they eventually passed into the hands of the Schriftgiesserei Stempel of Frankfurt am Main, where they are now preserved.*

Janson is an excellent example of the sturdy and influential Dutch old style types that prevailed throughout Europe during the seventeenth and early eighteenth centuries. It is highly legible, and its individual letters have a pleasing variety of design.

THE BOOK was composed, printed, and bound by H. Wolff, New York. Paper manufactured by P. H. Glatfelter, Spring Grove, Pa. Typography by Charles Farrell.